QUAKERS IN MEDICINE

'FRIENDS OF THE

CW00734851

Quakers in Medicine
'Friends of the Truth'

J.M.S. Pearce MD, FRCP
Emeritus Consultant Neurologist
Department of Neurology, Hull Royal Infirmary

William Sessions Limited
York, England

© J.M.S. Pearce 2009

ISBN 978-1-85072-388-2

Printed in 11 point Plantin Typeface
from Author's Disk
by Sessions of York
The Ebor Press
York, England

Contents

vi

List of Illustrations

Those two-dimensional works of art depicted here that are one hundred or more years old, are I believe in the public domain in the United States and in those countries with a copyright term of life of the author.

Preface

"If we have not quiet in our minds, outward comfort will do no more for us than a golden slipper on a gouty foot." John Bunyan (1628-1688)

MANY PUBLICATIONS attest to the achievements of Quakers as scientists. This short account is centred on the parts they played in Medicine.

George Fox, the founder of the Society of Friends, and his followers were seen as a challenge to the authority of the Anglican Church and were frequently harassed, arrested or imprisoned. Quakerism in the 17th and much of the 18th centuries was widely considered heretical, a threat to both church and state. Many of the great universities closed their doors to them, as did many secondary schools. Thus, in 18th and 19th century Medicine many were forced to seek their medical education abroad.

There were however, many Friends, or Quakers, as they became known, who were distinguished in the arts and sciences, although to achieve this end they had to struggle against formidable prohibitions that impeded their academic training in centres of learning. *The Quaker Truth Testimony* – the pursuit of truth determining many aspects of religion, science and history – has been a continuing theme that influenced them in their scientific and medical achievements and in the remarkable philanthropy and public service evident in so many of those described.

I attempt here to highlight the achievements and services of a small number of Quakers in some of the varied fields of British Medicine. Because there are numerous, more detailed biographies and bibliographies that are available for individual medical scientists, I have provided only selected references for the interested reader. Other writers would have chosen other people of equal merit. I can only hope that the reader, whether medical or non-medical by training, will consider that the men and women selected here fairly represent the development of Medicine in their time.

In each chapter, there are short accounts of the protagonists from their early roots and schooling, when known, to their professional progress and advances in diverse aspects of medical practice. Some of their more lasting contributions, publications, and the various honours they received are related. It is hoped that these essays will be of interest to those in non-medical and medical disciplines, for if those depicted reveal anything it is their wide areas of learning, often far beyond their medical contexts. Their lands of scholarship and knowledge were much broader in earlier times than they often are today. Those associated with them, often highly respected figures in their own right, have been briefly mentioned. Many comparable figures, not considered here, flourished and achieved fame in the United States and in many other countries. Those who have worked in the latter part of the 20th century have been deliberately omitted, since the historical importance of modern discoveries can seldom be properly assessed until many years have passed.

No distinction has been made those born into Quaker families from those who became converted to the faith, nor have I excluded those born Quakers, who for various reasons lapsed or failed regularly to attend the Friends Meetings. The selection is by no means comprehensive. But it aims to give the flavour of their attainments, hinting perhaps at the place their faith might have played in their various works and discoveries.

It is a pleasure to thank Bob Jarrett of William Sessions of York whose encouragement and efficiency have greatly facilitated the production of this book

J.M.S.P.
Anlaby, East Yorkshire
November 2008

CHAPTER 1

Introduction

GEORGE FOX (1624-1691), the founder of the Society of Friends was in his time viewed as a threat to the authority of the Anglican Church. Quakers were regarded as dissenters, and so he and his followers (known as Friends of the Truth) were frequently harassed, arrested or imprisoned. Quakers were in the 17th and much of the 18th centuries widely considered heretical dissenters, a threat to both Church and State. The Blasphemy Act of 1650 was the first of many legal moves against Quakers.[1] Since Quakers would neither take an oath nor subscribe to the Thirty-nine Articles of the Episcopal faith, the great universities closed their doors to them, as did many of the better secondary schools. At this time an estimated 21,000 Friends, or dissenters suffered because of their faith and 450 died in gaol. The names applied are illustrated in a book in the Quaker Collection at the University of Bradford, dated 1757. Its title page is revealingly worded:

> "A collection of Acts of Parliament and clauses of Acts of Parliament relative to those Protestant dissenters who are usually called by the name of Quakers ...". London : Luke Hinde, 1757.

The persecution of Fox and thousands of followers eventually was succeeded by greater religious tolerance. But not until 1871 did an act of Parliament revoke the religious tests applied to exclude those seeking entry to many Universities, including Oxford and Cambridge. So, put simply, those openly holding Quaker beliefs were widely persecuted and restricted in many of their endeavours.

Despite these barriers, and possibly partly because of them, many Quakers were forced into in the worlds of commerce, industry and philanthropy in which they frequently succeeded. In

1

London they attended three City of London Meetings: Bull and Mouth, Gracechuch and Devonshire House, and three Meetings outside the old London Wall: Peel, Wheeler Street and Bunhill. Of these, only the newest, Bunhill, still meets. Public service was their hallmark, even in the adverse, prevailing culture of persecution and prejudice. This is evident in diverse ways in the lives described here. There were many Friends, or Quakers, as they became known, who were distinguished in the arts and sciences. Just one of countless examples of their philanthropy was the legacy of the Quaker industrialist, Johns Hopkins, who left $7 million in 1873 for the foundation of both the University and Johns Hopkins Hospital (1889), in Baltimore. The University opened on February 22, 1876, and has produced many Nobel laureates, physicians, scientists and scholars of world renown. Quaker social service and philanthropy were eventually acknowledged when in 1947 the Nobel Peace prize was awarded to the Friends Service Council in Britain and the American Friends Service Committee, for their work for social justice and peace, including their relief work during and after the Second World War.

The Quaker ethos

The Quaker Truth Testimony – the pursuit of truth determining many aspects of religion, science and history – has been a continuing theme in Quaker history. The main countervailing force has been the 'over-respect for venerated authority: a deference to established conventions'.[2] The role of the Quaker ethos in moulding subsequent academic excellence, exemplified by the individuals highlighted here, is the subject of many books. It was summarised by K. Barry Sharpless in his Nobel lecture, 2001:

> I was educated in a Quaker school. The Quakers encourage modesty, thrift, initiative, and enterprise, but the greatest good is being a responsible member of the community – being useful. "Elegant" and "clever" were the chemical accolades of choice when I started doing research, just as "novel" is high praise now. Perhaps the Quakers are responsible for me valuing "useful" most.[3]

The brilliant Quaker astrophysicist Sir Arthur Eddington OM., FRS (1882-1944) similarly expressed the underlying spirit or philosophy that relates the faith of Friends to the disciplines of science:

2

"I think that the spirit of seeking is still the prevailing one in our faith, which for that reason is not embodied in any creed or formula… If so-called facts are changing shadows, they are shadows cast by the light of constant truth." (cited in Quaker faith & practice 26:16. Reflections, 1929: third edition)

Scientists and doctors

Many publications attest to the achievements of individual Quakers as scientists.[4,5] None however, collates the many contributions of Quakers to the art and science of medical practice. This account is centred on their roles in Medicine. Quaker scientists who contributed just as much to other aspects of knowledge include such luminaries as: John Bartram – "father of American Botany"; Jocelyn Bell Burnell, who discovered the first radio pulsars with Antony Hewish; Sir Francis Galton whose genius founded statistical methods, psychometrics, the first weather map, but who also invented the pernicious principles of eugenics; Kenneth E. Boulding, systems theorist and economist; George Ellis, who with Stephen Hawking wrote The Large Scale Structure of Space-Time; Luke Howard who initiated the nomenclature system for clouds; Lewis Fry Richardson, a famous Meteorologist; Len Lamerton, a founder of radiation biology, who measured the rate of growth of tumours; and Sir Arthur Eddington, courageous and brilliant astrophysicist.

I attempt here to highlight the main achievements and services of a small number of Quakers in several fields of British Medicine (Table 1). A more complete list abstracted from the Dictionary of National Biography (DNB) is shown for reference in Appendix 2. Because there are numerous, more detailed individual biographies and bibliographies available for individual medical scientists, I have provided only selected references for the interested reader. In a wide spectrum of Medicine, physicians, surgeons and basic scientists are prominent; but also included are those whose disciplines embraced genetics, physiology, pharmacology and pharmacy, and public health. In eras when specialisation had not developed, the endeavours of medical scientists commonly spread across more than one discipline; indeed, widely educated, brilliant polymaths were frequently encountered.

Many comparable figures, not considered here, flourished and achieved fame in the United States and in many other countries. No distinction has been made those born into Quaker families from those who became converted to the faith, nor have I excluded those who for various reasons lapsed, or failed regularly to attend the Friends Meetings. The selection is by no means comprehensive. But it aims to give the flavour and inventiveness of their works and discoveries, hinting perhaps at the place their faith might have played in their various endeavours and discoveries. Lacking detailed knowledge of religious philosophies, I have avoided idle conjectures in this area, which is considered in other texts referred to.

It is impossible but would be satisfying, if one could measure, the impact or importance of these talented men and women, but the extraordinary number who in different ways were recognised by election to The Royal Society, the highest accolade for any British scientist, speaks for itself. Election to the Royal Society is coveted because of the recognition it brings within scientific circles. Many Fellows will omit all other degrees and honours after their name in favour of the "simple" epithet FRS – in effect a scientific knighthood.

Remarkably, Arthur Raistrick claimed that between 1851 and 1900 English Quakers were more than 40 times as likely to be chosen as Fellows of the Royal Society, as non Quakers.[6] Why such enormous disproportion should have obtained is far from clear. After scrutiny of the records, Cantor indicates that many cited were not Quakers, and the statistics were often unreliable. For instance, William Penn was proposed by John Houghton at a meeting of the Royal Society on 2 November 1681, but was never formally admitted. Only nine are listed from the inception in 1660 until 1750. It is doubtful whether any major disproportion existed in the 19th and 20th centuries.

Quakers, Catholics and Jews, in pursuit of a career in 18th and 19th century Medicine were often forced by religious prejudices to seek their medical education abroad, notably in Leiden. Edinburgh, which was under secular not ecclesiastical control, did offer places and was attractive to Quakers, particularly since the Edinburgh MD was of high standing.

There are also those scientists, whose primary disciplines were not in Medicine, yet whose contributions to science directly or

4

indirectly impinged upon medical practice (Table 1). I have been able to include only a few such luminaries in a brief account that is not intended to be all embracing.

It will be understood that until the 20th century the figures portrayed here, had no access to the modern tools of medical science: no X-rays or scanning techniques, no sophis⁺icated biochemistry or microscopes, and tissue stains were primitive. They had to either invent their own often crude laboratory equipment or use their inferential intelligence to speculate upon the mysterious mechanisms of disease and its consequences. Given these severe strictures on prevailing knowledge, and poor technical implements, any medical historian will be intrigued and hugely impressed by the surprising accuracy and ingenuity of their discoveries and conclusions. If this leads to more than a hint of eulogy tinged with admiration, and if the foibles and failings of those considered are unwittingly minimised, the reader may allow the author a measure of indulgence.

Table 1
Quaker Scientists and Doctors

Name[†]	Main Contributions
Scientists who contributed to medical practice	
John Dalton FRS (1766-1844)	Atomic weight. Colour blindness (Daltonism).
William Allen FLS, FRS	First President The Pharmaceutical Society of Great Britain. Philanthropist. Educationalist. Social reformer.
Silvanus Phillips Thompson, FRS (1851-1916)	Electro-magnetism. Optics. Technical education.
Kathleen Yardley Lonsdale DSc., FRS (1903-1971)	Crystallographer. X-ray diffraction of crystals to determine structure of a molecule. Shape of benzene ring.

Name *cont.*	Main Contributions *cont.*
Dorothy Crowfoot Hodgkin OM, FRS (1910-1994)*	Crystallographer. Synthesised Penicillin, Insulin, Ferritin, & Vitamin B12.
Alan Lloyd Hodgkin KBE, OM, FRS (1914-1998)	Discoveries concerning transmission of the nerve impulse: the ionic mechanisms involved in excitation and inhibition of the nerve cell membrane.

Medical Scientists

John Fothergill MD, FRS (1712-1780)	Trigeminal neuralgia. Angina pectoris. diphtheria.
John Coakley Lettsom MD, FRCP (1744-1815)	Founded The Medical Society of London, 1773. Physician and philanthropist.
Caspar Wistar MD (1761-1818)	Physician and anatomist. President of American Philosophical Society. President of the Society for the Abolition of Slavery.
Thomas Young MD, FRS (1773-1829)	Young's modulus. Wave theory of light. Retinal cones the source of colour vision.
Joseph Jackson Lister FRS (1786-1869)	Microscopist. Father of Joseph Lister.
The Tuke family William Tuke (1732-1822) Henry Tuke (1755-1814) Samuel Tuke (1784-1857) James Hack Tuke (1819-1896) Daniel Hack Tuke MD (1827-1895)	Humane psychiatry: The Retreat at York.
Joseph Hodgson PRCS, FRS (1788-1869)	Versatile surgeon who founded Birmingham Eye Hospital. Aortic aneurysm.

Name *cont.*	**Main Contributions** *cont.*
Thomas Hodgkin MD (1798-1866)	Lymphoma (Hodgkin's disease). Anthropology. Anti-slavery movement.
Elizabeth Blackwell MD (1821-1910)	First female American/ English doctor, pioneer physician and campaigner.
Joseph, Lord Lister FRCS, FRS (1827-1912)	Surgeon. Initiated antiseptic surgery.
Sir Jonathan Hutchinson FRCS, FRS (1828-1913)	Ten volume Archives of Surgery (1885-99). Pegged teeth of congenital syphilitics. Hutchinson's fixed dilated pupil of temporal lobe coning.
Sir Rickman John Godlee KCVO, MS., FRCS (1849-1925)	Surgery of pulmonary infections. Removal of first English brain tumour. Biographer of Lord Lister.
William Allen Sturge (1850-1919)	Sturge Weber Kalischer syndrome.
Henry Head MD, FRCP, FRS (1861-1940)	Studies of Sensory nerves. Dermatomes. Aphasia.
Sir George Newman MD (1870-1948)	Infant Mortality. Editor, the Friends' Quarterly Examiner. Founded Friends' Ambulance.
Sir Joseph Barcroft CBE, MA, DSc., Hon. MD, Hon. FRCOG, FRS (1872-1947)	Physiologist. Respiratory function of blood. Foetal physiology.
Clark, Alfred Joseph MD, FRS (1885-1941)	Mode of action of Drugs on Cells. Classic pharmacology textbook.
Walter Russell, first Baron Brain (1895-1966)	Remote effects of cancer. Carpal tunnel syn. disorders of language & cognition.

Name *cont.*	Main Contributions *cont.*
Lionel Sharples Penrose MD, FRS (1898-1972)	Genetics of mental deficiency. Down's syndrome. Anti war campaigner.

†Arranged by date of birth

*Dorothy Hodgkin was not a Quaker, but is sneaked in here because of her close affiliations to Quaker attitudes and ethos, and her marriage into a Quaker family.

CHAPTER 2

John Dalton FRS (1766-1844)
Colour blindness (Daltonism); atomic weights; law of partial pressures

JOHN DALTON (Fig. 1) is one of the most famous and revered scientists of the last 250 years. He was the son of a Quaker weaver, born in Eaglesfield near Cockermouth in Cumbria. He was educated and then taught at a tiny schoolroom in Pardshaw Hall, the site of the Quaker Meeting House. At the age of ten he entered the service of a Quaker gentleman, Elihu Robinson, who taught him mathematics, and remarkably, by the age of twelve Dalton had acquired enough knowledge to set up a school for local children.

Fig. 1. *John Dalton. Engraved by Worthington after an 1814 painting by William Allen, published 25 June 1823 in Manchester and London.*

Fig. 2. *Stramongate School, Kendal.*

It did not prosper and in 1781 he joined his brother Jonathan, as a teacher in a school at Kendal (Fig. 2), which later they acquired. Dalton was already spending much time in study and by 1787 he delivered a course of lectures in natural philosophy. He learned Latin and Greek between 1782 and 1790 through an acquaintance, John Gough, whom Dalton regarded as a prodigy in scientific attainments.

It is hard to imagine how a humble schoolteacher could have acquired such a reputation, but in 1793, Dalton was appointed Professor of Mathematics and Natural Philosophy at New College, Manchester where he spent the rest of his life. He read a paper to the Manchester Literary and Philosophical Society: "Extraordinary Facts relating to the Vision of Colours" about colour blindness, which afflicted him and became known as *Daltonism*. He made substantial contributions to the understanding of meteorology. He showed that the total pressure of a gas mixture was the sum of the partial pressure of each gas. This established *Dalton's Law of Partial Pressures.*

Importantly, he was one of the first scientists to decide that all matter is made up of small particles, or atoms. Thus Dalton founded *Atomic Theory*. This theory assumes (1) that all matter is

10

made up of small indivisible and indestructible particles, called "atoms"; (2) all atoms are not alike, there being as many different sorts of atoms as there are elements; (3) the atoms constituting any one element are exactly alike and are of definite weight; and (4) that compounds are produced by the combination of different atoms. It follows that any definite compound (molecule) must consist of a definite assemblage of different atoms, and these atoms are of definite weight: whence the law of constant proportion. He calculated atomic weights from the percentage compositions of compounds, using an arbitrary system to determine the likely atomic structure of each compound. Using this system, he prepared the first table of atomic weights, which he published as: *A New System of Chemical Philosophy*, two volumes, (Manchester, 1808, 1810).

In 1822 Dalton was elected a Fellow of the Royal Society, and was a corresponding member of the French Academy of Sciences, and a co-founder of the British Association for the Advancement of Science. By the end of his life his atomic theory was universally accepted,[7] and in 1833 he was awarded an annual pension from the King.

His homemade equipment was thought to be crude, and his data not always exact, but his intelligent powers of deduction led him to discoveries of the highest importance. All modern understanding of chemistry as it relates to animal and human biology and physiology, ultimately is rooted in the identity of atomic structure and the closely related constitution of molecules. There has been no more valuable contribution to the fields of science.

He lived an abstemious and humble life as a lodger with the Rev. W John, in Faulkner Street, Manchester. He taught Mathematics in the Society of Friends Meeting House in George Street. He had few friends, and was unmarried. Dalton remained a solitary, perhaps unsocial man of simple needs and habits, his dress and manners fitting with his Quaker faith. He had a stroke in 1837 and a second one a year later, which impaired his speech. His final attack terminated his life on 27 July 1844. He was buried at Ardwick cemetery, Manchester.

At his death more than 40,000 people came to Manchester to pay their final respects. On Tuesday 14 October 2003, the Royal Society of Chemistry erected a bicentenary plaque (unveiled by

11

Nobel prize winner, Sir Harry Kroto) in Manchester Peace Gardens. Dalton and Sir Arthur Stanley Eddington share a green rectangular plaque (unveiled in 1998) at Stramongate School, Kendal, (Fig. 3) where Dalton taught. Eddington was born in Kendal and his father was Headmaster at the same school. There is a Dalton Street in Manchester city centre, a statue of him in the Town Hall entrance, and another outside the former Dalton College of Technology (now Manchester Metropolitan University) in Oxford Street. He is also the subject of a Ford Madox Brown mural in the Manchester Town Hall.

One might guess that this self-effacing, solitary genius would have been more than a little embarrassed by all the fuss.

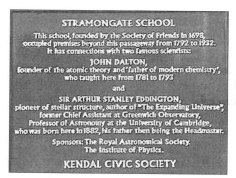

Fig. 3.
Dalton & Eddington plaque at Stramongate School, Kendal.

CHAPTER 3

Thomas Young MD, FRS (1773-1829)
Young's modulus; wave theory of light; retinal cones the source of colour vision

THOMAS YOUNG (Fig. 4) was both physician and physicist, who was responsible for important theories and discoveries in optics and in human anatomy that significantly affected future medical knowledge and practice. He was a remarkable polymath, who has on sound evidence been likened to Leonardo da Vinci. Little has survived of his personal life since many of his letters, journals and papers have disappeared.

Fig. 4. *Thomas Young. 1834* .

Young, the eldest of ten children, belonged to a Quaker family of Milverton, Somerset. His parents were 'stiff Quakers' towards whom he felt no warmth.[8] He spent much of his lonely childhood in the home of his grandparents. He owed to the Society of Friends he said, his powers of determination and perseverance whose influences can be seen in his later development. Before the age of fourteen Young had largely taught himself mathematics, Greek and Latin, Hebrew, and several Arabic languages. According to Crichton-Browne,[9] this unusually isolated nature of his youth may account for some of his unsympathetic style and rigidity.

He began to study Medicine in London in 1792, moved to Edinburgh in 1794, and a year later to Göttingen, where he obtained a Doctorate in Physics. In 1797 he entered Emmanuel College, Cambridge, where his polymathy caused him to be known as: "Phenomenon Young". While still in medical school, curious to discover how the eye focussed, he observed that an ox eye changed shape when focussing on near and distant objects. Shortly afterwards, a *Memoir on the structure of the Lens* was contributed to the Royal Society in May 1793, when he was aged only 20, and was followed by his election as FRS the next year. However, the celebrated anatomist, John Hunter claimed priority for the discovery, supported by Sir Everard Home and Mr Ramsden – an eminent optician. Hunter's claim was eventually disallowed by academia. Young also showed that the mechanism of astigmatism was a difference in degree of curvature of the two different meridians (i.e., the eye has different focal points in different planes) arising in the lens or cornea, in 1801.

A substantial inheritance made him financially independent, and in 1799 he established himself as a physician at 48 Welbeck Street, London (now recorded with a blue plaque) (Fig. 5). His Croonian lecture for 1808 was entitled: "Functions of the Heart and Arteries," He was appointed Physician to St. George's Hospital, London, in 1811. His medical writings included *An Introduction to Medical Literature, including a System of Practical Nosology* (1813) and *A Practical and Historical Treatise on Consumptive Diseases* (1815). He invented a simple rule to determine the correct dose of drugs for children, known as *Young's rule*: a child's dosage equals the adult dosage multiplied by the child's age in years, divided by the sum of 12 plus the child's age.

In the 1801, Young studied optical interference, observing that when a single light source is split into two beams, and the two beams

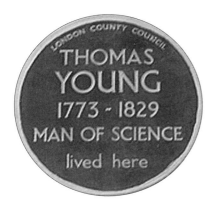

Fig. 5. *Thomas Young. Blue plaque at 48 Welbeck Street, London.*

are recombined by a lens, they produce a pattern of light and dark fringes. These fringes he cleverly deduced were caused by the beams of light behaving as waves with peaks and troughs. It "showed that light added to light could produce more light – or, most surprisingly, darkness". The interference pattern (*Young's fringes*) could only be explained by an "undulatory" or wave theory of light shown as alternating bands of light and dark. His first paper on Wave Theory led to his appointment as Professor of Natural Philosophy at the Royal Institution on 20 January 1801. By 17 May he had delivered no less than 31 lectures, and by the end of 1802 he had given 60, which were published four years later as *A Course of Lectures on Natural Philosophy and the Mechanical Arts*. This was one of the 'sacred' books of Physical Science; its expositions have never been excelled.

He then applied his new *Wave Theory Of Light* to explain the colours of thin films of soap bubbles. By relating colour to wavelength, he calculated the approximate wavelengths of the seven colours recognized by Newton. Since these theories differed from Newton's doctrines, at first many scientists resisted them. Like Hermann von Helmholtz (1821-1894)*, inventor of the ophthalmoscope, his work caused him to suggest three different sets of

---

* Helmholtz was born at Potsdam. His father, Ferdinand, was a teacher of philology and philosophy, while his mother was a Hanoverian, a lineal descendant of William Penn. He graduated in Medicine from the military medical school in Berlin, 1843. He wrote in 1847 what has been described as one of the great scientific papers of the 19th century: *Über die Erhaltung der Kraft* [On the conservation of energy].

nerve cells or cones in the retina, each sensitive to a primary colour: red, blue or green. This became known as the *Young-Helmholtz trichromatic theory*. The modern understanding of optics and eye diseases rests heavily on these discoveries.

Young's varied experiments in physics were outstanding in their originality and quickly achieved general acceptance. He measured the size of molecules, surface tension in liquids, and quantities of elasticity. He proposed a constant in the mathematical equation describing elasticity, known as *Young's modulus*. He wrote many important and original papers including a 560 page monograph on classification of diseases: *An introduction to medical literature, including a system of practical nosology ...*, (Fig. 6) which was controversial and inevitably, soon became outdated.

A versatile physician and scientist, he mastered languages and hieroglyphics, enabling him to study Egyptology. This led him to examine the Rosetta Stone in 1814. After investigating other hieroglyphic writings, he produced an important translation.

So why is Young not better known? One reason is that he chose – after early work was unjustly excoriated by the jealous critic Brougham (later Lord Brougham) – to write many articles anonymously, believing "it will do better without my name on it". His lectures though excellent in content were so condensed that many failed to understand his arguments. His explanations of his theories were also frequently laconic to the point of obscurity. In his later lifestyle, he gradually abandoned several Quaker traditions, but remained self-effacing, unwilling to display his inner but profound enthusiasms.

His contemporary Sir John Herschel called him a "truly original genius". His epitaph in Westminster Abbey fittingly describes him as:

"a man alike eminent in almost every department of human learning."

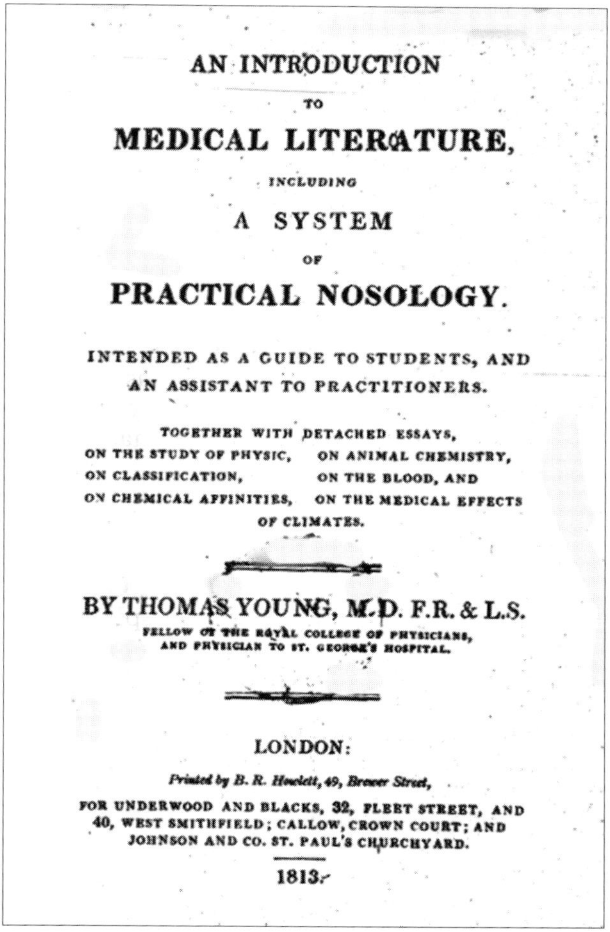

AN INTRODUCTION

TO

MEDICAL LITERATURE,

INCLUDING

A SYSTEM

OF

PRACTICAL NOSOLOGY.

INTENDED AS A GUIDE TO STUDENTS, AND
AN ASSISTANT TO PRACTITIONERS.

TOGETHER WITH DETACHED ESSAYS,
ON THE STUDY OF PHYSIC,   ON ANIMAL CHEMISTRY,
ON CLASSIFICATION,   ON THE BLOOD, AND
ON CHEMICAL AFFINITIES,   ON THE MEDICAL EFFECTS
OF CLIMATES.

BY THOMAS YOUNG, M.D. F.R. & L.S.

FELLOW OF THE ROYAL COLLEGE OF PHYSICIANS,
AND PHYSICIAN TO ST. GEORGE'S HOSPITAL.

LONDON:

Printed by B. R. Howlett, 49, Brewer Street,

FOR UNDERWOOD AND BLACKS, 32, FLEET STREET, AND
40, WEST SMITHFIELD; CALLOW, CROWN COURT; AND
JOHNSON AND CO. ST. PAUL'S CHURCHYARD.

1813.

Fig. 6. *Thomas Young. Frontispiece, An Introduction to
Medical Literature, 1813.*

17

CHAPTER 4

William Allen FRS, FLS (1770-1843)
First President of The Pharmaceutical Society of Great Britain; philanthropist; educationalist; social reformer

WILLIAM ALLEN (Fig. 7) is a good example of the grey areas in which Medicine and Science overlap. He was not a medical doctor but the pharmaceutical industry he created was to be of great benefit to patients and to medical practice.

The eldest son of Job and Margaret (Stafford) Allen, he was born at Spitalfields, London on 29 August 1770. His father was a silk manufacturer and a devout Quaker. William went to school in

Fig. 7. *William Allen.*

Rochester, Kent. Showing an inquisitive intelligence, in 1792, he was a humble clerk, but for his own interest attended lectures at Guy's Hospital and St. Thomas's Hospital. He also sought out meetings of various scientific societies. In 1794, he became a member of the Chemical and Physical Societies of Guy's Hospital. In 1795, he became a partner in the chemical (pharmaceutical) company where he worked. It was then named Mildred and Allen. In 1796, Allen joined a group of scientists to establish the now long forgotten *Askesian Society:* a club designed to promote scientific experimentation. Members had to present a paper or else pay a fine, which resulted in Luke Howard's famous 1802 presentation 'On The Modification of Clouds', the first attempt to name and classify cloud formations.

In 1797 his company became Allen and Howard when he joined with his friend and partner Luke Howard; they later set up another pharmaceutical research laboratory in Plaistow. The earlier premises were sited at Plough Court off Lombard Street in the City of London, following its Quaker beginnings under the apothecary, Silvanus Bevan (1691-1765). Howard too was a Quaker pharmacist, who is best known for devising a Linnaean nomenclature system for clouds, which he proposed in an 1802 presentation to the Askesian Society. He was elected FRS in 1821. Their joint pharmaceutical enterprise flourished. But Allen and Howard separated in 1806. Later that year Allen married Charlotte Hanbury and eventually the firm became the well respected and commercially successful Allen and Hanbury's until it was acquired by Glaxo Wellcome in the 1980s.

In 1802 Allen was elected a Fellow of the Linnaean Society and in 1803 he was made president of the Physical Society at Guy's. On April 15, 1841 William Allen, with Jacob Bell, Daniel Hanbury, John Bell and other London chemists founded the Pharmaceutical Society of Great Britain. Allen was its first President. The premises were at 17 Bloomsbury Square, where a School of Pharmacy was established in which botany and *materia medica* were vital parts of the curriculum. Its standing was recognised when in 1843, Queen Victoria granted the Society its Royal Charter.

Taking counsel from Humphry Davy and John Dalton, Allen accepted an invitation to become a lecturer at the Royal Institution. In 1807, his original research on carbon enabled him to be proposed successfully for election to Fellowship of the Royal Society (elected on 19 November 1807), which brought him into contact with many distinguished scientific researchers. His application stated: "Professor of Natural Philosophy in the Royal Institution & Fellow of the Linnaean Society, a Gentleman well versed in various branches of Philosophical knowledge."

His interests, however, moved from science to philanthropy.[10] From an early age he had been concerned with the needy. His philanthropic work was closely allied to his religious beliefs, A grave national shortage of food in 1796 led to a crisis. Allen therefore started the Soup Society to provide sustenance for the starving poor, a scheme later adopted for cholera epidemics. But the evil of slavery and horrors of war also gravely troubled him. He was elected to membership of the Committee of the Society for the Abolition of the Slave Trade in 1805. He was a founder of the Peace Society in 1810. When the slave trade was banned in 1807, Allen became an active member of the African Institution, and campaigned for the abolition of black slavery in Sierra Leone and the West Indies.

He was keen to promote progressive education. Thus, he was a member of the committee formed in 1808 for the support of the profligate Joseph Lancaster, the founder of the progressive school at Borough Road, Southwark, which in 1814 became the British and Foreign School Society. Allen was its treasurer. He persuaded the committee to settle Lancaster's debts; he pruned the monitorial institution's extravagances, raised subscriptions, and removed Lancaster from control of the institution. He played a leading part in the production of the British Society's teaching manual and wrote the preface to Scripture Lessons (1820) based on extracts from the Bible.

Allen displayed many acts of public service. With help from James Mill, in 1811 he started a quarterly journal for social reforms, quaintly titled: *The Philanthropist: Or Repository for Hints and Suggestions Calculated to Promote the Comfort and Happiness of Man.* It published articles by, *inter alia*, Mill and Jeremy Bentham and survived till 1817.

Whilst travelling abroad with his wife Charlotte in 1816, she became seriously ill and died. But two years later he set out again to visit Europe with the Quaker evangelist Stephen Grellet. On his return, he worked to establish, and run from 1824 to 1838, a Quaker school for girls at Fleetwood House. It could boast extensive grounds at Stoke Newington that is now part of Abney Park Cemetery. He was re-married in 1827 to a wealthy widow, Grizell Birbeck, thereby provoking a satirical cartoon by Cruickshank – said to have depicted Allen and his future wife in 'Newington Nunnery', the Quaker girl's school. He toured Europe again in 1840 for five months accompanied by Elizabeth Fry and the banker, Samuel Gurney.

William Allen died at Lindfield, Sussex on 30 December 1843, and was buried at Stoke Newington, London, in the grounds of the Yoakley Road Quaker Meeting House – now a Seventh Day Adventist chapel.

William Allen was responsible for no major academic advances in science, yet his early investigations must have been highly esteemed as witnessed by election to the Royal Society. This appears even more remarkable when one considers his lack of higher academic University education. Through his success in pharmaceuticals, he brought substantial benefits to patients by means of several drugs; and his promotion of educational methods was a significant advance. In many ways, he epitomises the Quaker devotion to countering poverty, slavery, and poor educational resources by using his hard earned personal wealth.

CHAPTER 5

Silvanus Phillips Thompson, FRS (1851–1916)
Electro-magnetism; optics; technical education; X-rays

SILVANUS THOMPSON (Fig. 8) was born in 1851 to a Quaker family in York. His father taught at the Quaker School at Bootham in York. In 1873 Silvanus Thompson was made the science master at Bootham School.

He became increasingly interested in light, optics and electro-magnetism. In 1876 he was appointed as a lecturer in Physics at

Fig. 8. *Silvanus Phillips Thompson.*

University College, Bristol, and later was made Professor in 1878 at the early age of 27. His lecturing skills were in great demand. In 1881 he published *Elementary Lessons in Electricity and Magnetism*, reprinted 16 times in 12 years. Two other courses of lectures were published as books: *Dynamo-Electric Machinery* (1882), and *The Electro-magnet and Electromagnetic Mechanism* (1891). He tried to enlighten the lay public by writing *Calculus made Easy* by " F.R.S." in 1910. All of these teachings and texts were important to aspiring scientists and to students of Medicine in their preclinical work.

Another major interest related to technical education and the deficiencies in them that he observed. For much of his life he attempted to remedy these problems, notably at the newly founded Finsbury Technical College, created by the City and Guilds Institute. Thompson was appointed Principal and Professor of Physics in 1878 and remained there for the next 30 years. He wrote many biographical works, including: *Michael Faraday His Life and Work* 1898, *The life of Lord Kelvin* 1910, and in 1901, translated from Latin Dr. William Gilbert's *De Magnete, Magneticisque Corporibus*, (1600). In this work Gilbert described his experiments with his model earth called the terrella. From the experiments, he came to the remarkable conclusion that the Earth was a giant magnet and that this was why the compass pointed north.

Thompson attended and lectured at the Royal Institution giving the Christmas lectures in 1896 on Light, Visible and Invisible, with an account of Roentgen Light (X-rays). He was elected a Fellow of the Royal Society in 1889.

He repeated Roentgen's experiments immediately after his discovery of X-rays was announced in Britain; he gave the first public demonstration of the new X-rays at the Clinical Society of London on March 30, 1896. Demonstrating the medical significance of his display of Roentgen's experiments, Dr William Hale White said:

"The audience was thrilled, most seeing for the first time actual pieces of bones and metal. Silvanus Thompson was a prince among lecturers. I have never heard a better demonstration or attended a more memorable medical meeting."

He was elected first President of the Roentgen Society (later the British Institute of Radiology).

Thompson was said to be almost obsessed by the truth. In 1915 he delivered the Swarthmore Lecture to the Society of Friends entitled: The Quest for Truth, He remained an active member of the Religious Society of Friends, until his death in London on June 12, 1916. A blue plaque commemorates his name at the Engineer's Club, Bristol.(Fig. 9)

Fig. 9. *Silvanus Phillips Thompson. Blue Plaque at Engineer's Walk, Bristol.*

CHAPTER 6

Kathleen Lonsdale DSc., FRS
(1903-1971)

X-ray diffraction of crystals to determine the structure of a molecule; studies of benzene ring; structure of drugs and urinary stones

KATHLEEN LONSDALE (Fig. 10) was one of the women pioneers in a man's world of professional scientists.[11] She was born Kathleen Yardley in Newbridge, Co. Kildare in Ireland, the youngest of ten children. The family had no Quaker roots: her father, Harry, was a retired soldier working as a postmaster; her mother Jessie was a Scottish Baptist. The family was poor.

Fig. 10. *Kathleen Lonsdale.*

After marital upheaval, her mother moved to Essex, where Kathleen won a scholarship to the County High School for Girls at Ilford; then won a County scholarship as well as the Royal Geographical Society's medal, which enabled her to attend Bedford College for Women, in London, at the age of 16, to study mathematics.[12] She won a University scholarship and changed from mathematics to physics. In 1922 she came first in the honours B.Sc. examination, and the eminent crystallographer W.H. Bragg was so impressed that he offered her a place in his research group at University College, London. Kathleen used X-ray diffraction to determine the structure of a molecule by analysing how a crystal formed by that molecule would scatter a beam of X-rays. In 1923 Bragg moved to the Royal Institution and took Kathleen Yardley with him.

Kathleen met her future husband Thomas Lonsdale when he was a research student at University College. In 1927 they married and moved to Leeds where she was appointed Amy Lady Tate Scholar and part-time demonstrator at the University. Whilst in Leeds, gravely troubled by the evils of warfare, she became a Quaker. At the outbreak of the second World War she became a conscientious objector, and like many Quakers was summoned, fined and sent to prison. She served her time for one month in Holloway gaol.

It was in Leeds that Kathleen investigated crystals of hexamethyl benzene to show that the benzene ring (an essential component of most organic compounds) is flat, and she calculated its dimensions.[13] In 1930, she went to the Royal Institution laboratories in London and remained there for 15 years. She obtained the D.Sc., University College, London in 1936. On 22 March 1945 Kathleen Lonsdale and Marjory Stephenson were the first women to be elected Fellows of the Royal Society. She was also the first woman President of the British Association for the Advancement of Science. She was awarded in 1957 the Davy Medal of the Royal Society and three years later became its Vice-President. From 1960-66 she was Vice-President, and in 1966, President of the International Union of Crystallography. In 1968 she was appointed President of the British Association for the Advancement of Science, and Emeritus Professor, University College, London.

In her later years she expanded her work into solid state reactions,* pharmacological compounds, and the constitution of bladder and renal stones. These were just a few of her discoveries, which found clinical application. She edited the International Atlas for X-ray Crystallography. Kathleen Lonsdale wrote many esteemed papers including a monograph *Crystals and x rays*, 1948.[14] She trained countless students in the techniques and made many contributions to science and indirectly to Medicine.

She vigorously promoted pacifism and supported the foundation of the Pugwash Movement.** She served as Vice-President of the Atomic Scientist's Association and President of the Women's International League for Peace and Freedom. In popular demand as a scientific speaker, she lectured also on non-scientific topics in Britain and abroad. These often included science and religion, and the role of women in science.

In 1965 she was created a Dame Commander of the Order of the British Empire (DBE). When her husband retired in 1960, they worked together for peace and prison reform. In 1970 she developed leukaemia and died in hospital on April 1st, 1971.

She is commemorated in her native Kildare at the National University of Ireland, Maynooth, by the Lonsdale Prize, awarded to the student obtaining the best First Class Honours degree in Chemistry. In 1981 the Chemistry building at University College, was renamed the Kathleen Lonsdale Building in her honour and in 1998 the new Aeronautical and Environmental Building at the University of Limerick was officially named the Kathleen Lonsdale Building, marking her Irish birth.

Her contemporary and friend, Dorothy Hodgkin, Nobel Laureate in Chemistry 1964, said of her:

"There is a sense in which she appeared to own the whole of crystallography in her time."

---

* The study of the structure and physical properties of solids, used in synthesis of drugs and their physical and chemical transformations.
** The Pugwash Conferences take their name from the location of the first meeting, held in 1957 in the village of Pugwash, Nova Scotia, Their aim was to bring together, from around the world, influential scholars and public figures concerned with reducing the danger of armed conflict.

CHAPTER 7

Dorothy Crowfoot Hodgkin OM, FRS (1910-1994)

Crystallographer; synthesised penicillin;
insulin & vitamin B12

THOUGH NOT a Quaker by religion, her marriage to the Quaker Thomas Lionel Hodgkin and her personal pacifist ethics were so closely aligned to the Quaker attitudes, that she is included here. Her contributions to Medicine were of immense importance.

Dorothy Hodgkin (Fig. 11) was one of the main founders of protein crystallography.[15] She possessed a unique mixture of skills

Fig. 11. *Dorothy Hodgkin.*

that allowed her to extend the use of X-rays to reveal the structures of compounds that were far more complex than anything attempted before.

Dorothy Crowfoot was born in 1910 in Cairo. Her father was an archaeologist serving with the Egyptian Ministry of Education. Her mother was an amateur botanist and artist. In 1914 she and her sisters came to England where she attended Sir John Leman Grammar School in Beccles, Suffolk. Aged ten, after observing crystals formed from copper sulphate and alum she was inspired and later wrote: " I was captured for life, by chemistry and by crystals." For her sixteenth birthday her mother gave her a book by the world renowned Sir William Henry Bragg, entitled, *Concerning the Nature of Things*, which explained how scientists used x-rays to study atoms and molecules. It was no surprise that she read chemistry at Somerville College, Oxford, then studied at Cambridge with John Desmond Bernal, a distinguished researcher, who incidentally was a communist. He developed her interest in x-ray crystallography to demonstrate the structure of proteins. She greatly admired him naming him "Sage". In 1937 she married Thomas Lionel Hodgkin (1910-1982), author and active Marxist. He was a Quaker, son of Robin H. Hodgkin, provost of Queen's College, Oxford and cousin of A.L. Hodgkin, the Nobel Prize winner for Medicine in 1963. Though not a Communist, Dorothy's attraction to leftist politics was on humanitarian grounds: on world peace, resolution of conflicts by meetings of prominent scientists, and alleviation of the economically down-trodden. She clearly epitomised all the traditional Quaker values, but did not formally belong to the Society of Friends.

One morning in May 1940, Hodgkin had a chance meeting with an unusually animated Ernst Chain outside the Dunn School of Pathology in Oxford. Chain told Hodgkin that he and his colleague Howard Florey had just discovered something amazing. Florey and Chain were experimenting with penicillin, the bacteria-killing substance that Alexander Fleming had somewhat fortuitously discovered in moulds in 1928. Since Fleming's discovery, several researchers had tried and failed to purify and synthesise active forms of penicillin, and had erroneously decided that penicillin might be interesting to the bacteriologist but would have little practical application in Medicine, until the vital experiment that so excited Chain.[16]

Chain realised that knowledge of the molecular structure of penicillin would be crucial. He promised her: "Some day we will have crystals for you." After years of intensive work at Somerville College, Oxford, on Victory in Europe Day, 8 May 1945, with thousands of people packing the streets to celebrate, Dorothy Hodgkin made her way through the cheering crowds. For in her hands she clutched a model of wires and corks so frail that she struggled to protect it from the celebrations. Yet the information within this model would help to treat the infections of countless people across the world. From an amorphous penicillin mould, she had discovered the precise chemical structure and thereby created the model of penicillin. As Ernst Chain declared in his Nobel Lecture: "For the first time the structure of a whole molecule has been calculated from X-ray data, and it is the more remarkable that this should have been possible in the case of a substance having the complexity of the penicillin molecule." This knowledge of the structure[17] finally allowed the synthesis of pure penicillin and its many derivatives, such as ampicillin and the cephalosporins (derived from sewage sludge), which formed the foundations of future antibiotic treatments.

Not until another seventeen years of hard work had passed did she solve the structure of vitamin B 12., the vitamin deficient in pernicious anaemia,[18] and her just reward of the Nobel Prize for Chemistry in 1964 for this work: "for her determinations by X-ray techniques of the structures of important biochemical substances". She was only the third woman to win the Nobel Prize in Chemistry. And, in 1965, she became the first woman to be given the Order of Merit. In 1976 Dr. Hodgkin was awarded the Royal Society's Copley Medal. She was Chancellor of Bristol University, 1970-88. She received the Lenin Peace Prize, and the freedom of Beccles, the town of much of her childhood, where Dorothy Hodgkin Court, and a monument stand in her honour.

She always gave her name as plain Dorothy Hodgkin, and insisted that her junior colleagues call her simply, Dorothy. When she retired, she continued to work for world peace and was President of the British Association for the Advancement of Science. In 1983 she was a Fellow of Wolfson College, Oxford. She suffered uncomplainingly from rheumatoid arthritis for most of her adult life. A set of British stamps issued in August 1996 acknowledged five 'Women of Achievement'; Dorothy Hodgkin was one of them. In her life she had determined the three-dimensional structures of: cholesterol, penicillin, vitamin B12, lactoglobulin, ferritin and insulin. She died of a stroke in the lovely Cotswold village of Shipston-on-Stour on 29 July 1994.

In the distinguished Biotechnologist M. Vijayan's memorial to her, he made an analogy with Mahatma Gandhi of whom Albert Einstein said:

"Generations to come, it may be, will scarce believe that such a one as this ever in flesh and blood walked upon this earth."

Vijayan commented: "With all of her accomplishments, awards, and contributions to modern science, such can be said of Dorothy Crowfoot Hodgkin".

Medical Doctors

THE MEDICAL contributions included here have been restricted to those originating in Britain. But, Quaker doctors practised in America, as physicians and surgeons, as well as researchers in many fields of laboratory Medicine. Quaker doctors of importance also practised in other European and Asian countries. Many of those in America graduated after the notable arrival from England of William Penn (1621-1718), the prominent Quaker who accompanied George Fox on his many travels. New England Puritans, were hostile to Quakers – as were British Anglicans. In 1677, a group of prominent Quakers that included Penn purchased the colonial province of West New Jersey. Two hundred settlers from Chorleywood and Rickmansworth in Hertfordshire and from nearby Buckinghamshire arrived, and founded the town of Burlington. In 1682, East New Jersey was also purchased by Quakers.

Penn eventually emigrated to America where he founded the colony of Pennsylvania. In 1681, King Charles II had granted a land charter to William Penn, in honour of his father, Admiral Sir William Penn. William landed in 1682, almost 300 years before this author boarded in a school house, bearing his name. There are countless surgeons and physicians of Quaker families who have contributed to the practice of Medicine in its many aspects in the US, following William Penn's arrival. Only a few of the outstanding British men and women and their attainments can be outlined here for space does not allow an appraisal of them all.

CHAPTER 8

John Fothergill MD, FRS (1712-1780)
Trigeminal neuralgia; angina pectoris; diphtheria; plant hunter

JOHN FOTHERGILL (Fig. 12) was an English physician, plant collector, and philanthropist. Born of Quaker parents at Carr End, a moorland farm near Bainbridge, Wensleydale, in Yorkshire. He was the son of John Fothergill (1676-1745), a preacher and farmer, and Margaret Hough. After studying at the famous Sedbergh School until 1728, Fothergill was apprenticed to his fellow Quaker apothecary, botanist and minister, Benjamin Bartlett of Bradford.

Fig. 12. *John Fothergill.*

He moved to Edinburgh in 1734, taking the Edinburgh M.D. in 1736, followed by further studies at St Thomas's Hospital, London. He was admitted a Licentiate of the London College of Physicians on 1st October, 1744, and was the first graduate in Medicine of the University of Edinburgh to be admitted by the London College. After visiting Europe in 1740, he settled in London. He lived in Gracechurch Street in the city but moved to Harpur Street, Bloomsbury in 1767 where he established a thriving practice. Always industrious, in the epidemics of influenza in 1795 and 1776 he is said to have attended sixty patients daily.

Trigeminal neuralgia

John Locke, the famous physician and philosopher, had described in a series of letters to Dr John Mapletoft in 1677[19] an excruciatingly painful condition of the face afflicting the Countess of Northumberland. But its distinctive nature was not generally recognised, and often mistaken for toothache. In 1756, Nicolas André reported two cases, which he termed *tic douloureux*, because of the painful contraction of the face in attacks. Fothergill's description *Of A Painful Affection of The Face** was presented to the Medical Society in London in 1773. The accuracy of his observations merits repeating here:

> "...The pain comes suddenly and is excruciating; it lasts but a short time, perhaps a quarter or half a minute, and then goes off; it returns at irregular intervals, sometimes in half an hour, sometimes there are two or three repetitions in a few minutes. Eating will bring it on some persons. Talking, or the least motion of the muscles of the face affects others; the gentlest touch of a hand or a handkerchief will sometimes bring on the pain."

He had met with 14 cases and metaphorically attributed the cause to a 'cancerous acrimony', because of the persistence and incurability of the pain. It was widely known as *Fothergill's disease*.[20]

A highly successful London practice afforded him many opportunities. He described angina pectoris (chest pain caused by coronary artery disease) in 1776, eight years after Heberden. Not only

---

* Fothergill J. Of a painful affection of the face. Medical observations and inquiries by a society of physicians. London, 1773; 5: 129-142 [This publication was funded privately by Fothergill from 1771-1776. It is included in Complete Works of John Fothergill, a copy in library of RCP London].

was he a distinguished Quaker physician, but also a renowned plant hunter. Fothergill's book, *Account of the Sore Throat attended with Ulcers* (1748), described epidemic scarlet fever, and contained one of the earliest accounts of diphtheria in English. The first printing sold out in a few weeks; several editions followed, and it was translated into several languages. Migraine, often known as megrim or sick headache, also attracted his attention. He wrote an important and discursive account of migraine : *Remarks on that complaint commonly known under the name of sick headach*[21] in 1784 (Fig. 13).

Fothergill cared for rich and poor alike. Amongst his more famous patients were: Clive of India, John Wesley, Fletcher Norton, the Speaker of the House of Commons, Lord Dartmouth, later Secretary of State for the American Colonies, the Penn family – proprietors of Pennsylvania, and Benjamin Franklin. Such dignitaries are listed not in blind veneration, but to suggest the esteem in which he was held.

He spent much of his earnings on acts of philanthropy, and in the establishment of his botanical garden at Upton, Essex, that was renowned all over Europe, for many rare perennials and shrubs which he collected from distant lands. It included 3400 species of conservatory plants. The estate later became West Ham Park. Carolus Linnaeus (1707-1778) gave the scientific name *Fothergilla* to a genus of witch hazel that Fothergill brought from America to Essex. His large collection of rare shells and minerals, acquired over many years, were bought on his death by the famous anatomist, Dr William Hunter.

In 1743 he became the correspondent from the English Friends' yearly Meeting to the Philadelphia Meeting. Because of his many influential American contacts and friends, he became a valued political adviser to the Quaker members of the Pennsylvania assembly. In 1757 the assembly sent Benjamin Franklin to London, but he quickly fell ill and was sent as a patient to Fothergill. They became good friends and collaborators, and he generously supported many American young doctors. With Benjamin Franklin, he tried unsuccessfully to avert the Revolutionary War. A further indication of his continued commitment can be seen when in 1777 Fothergill turned to the Quaker banker, David Barclay for help in founding Ackworth School in Pontefract, Yorkshire. In a letter to Franklin, dated 25 October 1780, he described it as 'a school for a plain English education for the sons and daughters of poor Friends'.[22] Fothergill paid for A translation of the Bible (1764) by Anthony Purver, a Quaker.

Margaret DeLacy's article on Fothergill relates:

"Among Fothergill's Edinburgh friends was the surgeon William Hunter, who settled in London about 1746; they

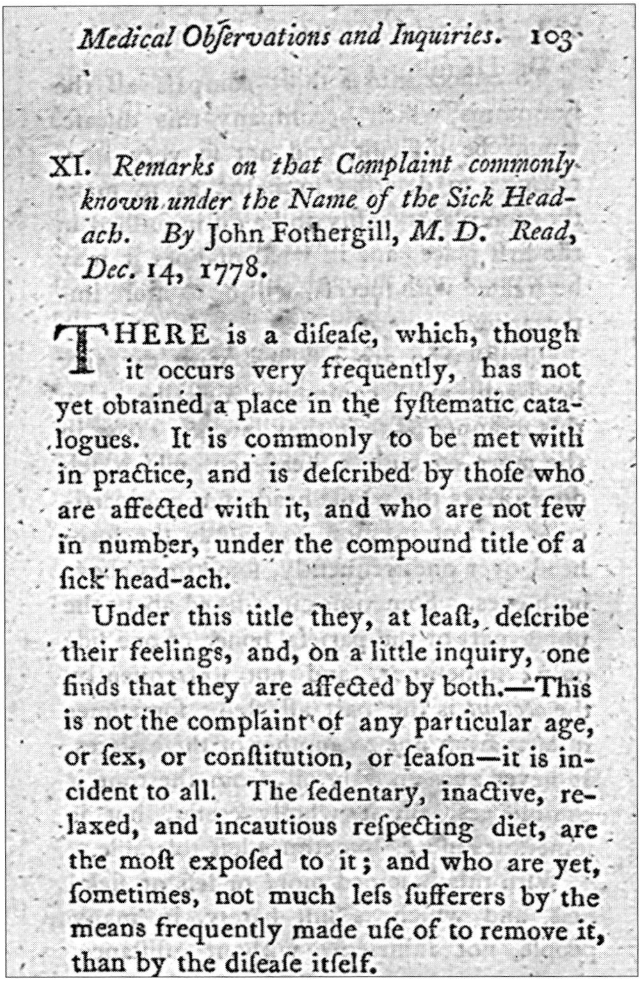

Medical Obſervations and Inquiries. 103

XI. *Remarks on that Complaint commonly known under the Name of the Sick Head-ach. By* John Fothergill, *M. D. Read, Dec.* 14, 1778.

THERE is a diſeaſe, which, though it occurs very frequently, has not yet obtained a place in the ſyſtematic catalogues. It is commonly to be met with in practice, and is deſcribed by thoſe who are affected with it, and who are not few in number, under the compound title of a ſick head-ach.

Under this title they, at leaſt, deſcribe their feelings, and, on a little inquiry, one finds that they are affected by both.—This is not the complaint of any particular age, or ſex, or conſtitution, or ſeaſon—it is incident to all. The ſedentary, inactive, relaxed, and incautious reſpecting diet, are the moſt expoſed to it; and who are yet, ſometimes, not much leſs ſufferers by the means frequently made uſe of to remove it, than by the diſeaſe itſelf.

Fig. 13. *John Fothergill's 'Sick Headach'.*

collaborated on many efforts, including the formation in 1754 of a society of physicians modelled on the Edinburgh Medical Society. Between 1757 and 1784 this group, which never adopted an official name, published six volumes of transactions under the title Medical Observations and Inquiries."

This private conclave of a few hospital physicians was recorded informally as 'A Society of London Physicians', and should not to be confused with the 'Medical Society of London' founded by Lettsom in 1773 (*vide infra*).

A glimpse of Dr. Fothergill, the man, can be seen in the diary* of his 17-year-old niece, Betty Fothergill, who spent the winter of 1769-70 in her uncle's household.[23] She related:

"Surely, he is the first of men. With the becoming dignity of age he unites the cheerfulness and liberality of youth. He possesses the most virtues and the fewest failings of any man I know".[24]

In *Literary Anecdotes of the Eighteenth Century*; (London, Nichols, son and Bentley, 1815) he is described:

"His features were all expressive, and his eye had a peculiar brilliancy. There was a charm in his conversation and address that conciliated the regard and confidence of all who employed him; and so discreet and uniform was his conduct, that he was not apt to forfeit the esteem, which he had once acquired. At his meals he was uncommonly abstemious…By this uniform and steady temperance he preserved his mind vigorous and active…"

A licentiate only, of the London Royal College of Physicians, he was elected Fellow of the Edinburgh College of Physicians in 1754, and in 1763 became a Fellow of the Royal Society. He died in 1780 from a second attack of 'suppression of urine' [retention] and was buried in the Quaker burial ground at Winchmore-Hill. Seventy carriages attended his funeral procession. The frontispiece of the first posthumous edition of his works (1781) depicts him as the Good Samaritan. Hogarth's cabinet portrait is in the London College of Physicians.

---

* Elizabeth [Betty] Fothergill (1752-1809) later Chorley: diary 1769-70 3 vols, Archives, Religious Society Of Friends S.51.

John Fothergill inspired and encouraged many aspiring young doctors. He was mentor to John Haygarth FRS (1740-1827), who introduced important measures for preventing infectious fevers;[25] and John Coakley Lettsom was his protégé. His nephew, Samuel Fothergill (1780-1822) MD, Glasgow in 1802 was a Quaker doctor, who with Wm Royston, edited the London Medical and Physical Journal. He too wrote about trigeminal neuralgia in: *An account of a Painful Affection of the nerves of the Face, commonly called Tic Douloureux*. London. 1804.

Amongst John Fothergill's descendants were: John Milner Fothergill (1841-1888), a physician and author, born at Morland, Westmorland, the son of George Fothergill, a surgeon apothecary. Dr Anthony Fothergill (1732-1814) was born at Sedbergh, became MD, FRCP, FRS and practised in Northampton, in London in John Fothergill's house at Harpur Street, in Bath, and in Philadelphia. A physician and medical author of distinction, and an intimate 'friend' of John, he claimed 'no consanguinity'. One may suspect he was related, possibly a cousin who wished to avoid any accusation of nepotism.

John Coakley Lettsom MD, FRCP Ed, FRS (1744-1815)

Physician who founded The Medical Society of
London; reflections on the general treatment
and cure of fevers

JOHN COAKLEY Lettsom (sometimes spelled Lettsome) (Fig.
14) was born into the Quaker community on the island of Van Dyke
in the British Virgin Islands, in 1744, son of Edward and Mary
Lettsom. He was sent to a Quaker school at Penketh near
Warrington, Lancashire, at the age of six. There he impressed the

Fig. 14. *Dr. John Coakley Lettsome
(1744-1815).*

Quaker preacher Samuel Fothergill, who became his guardian and introduced him to his celebrated brother, the physician, Dr John Fothergill*. In 1761 he journeyed by packhorse to Settle in Yorkshire as apprentice to Abraham Sutcliffe, a Quaker apothecary. Lettsom's main recreation was walking in the Yorkshire Dales and collecting minerals, fossils and plants. Thirty years later his mineral collection of 700 specimens became an early element of Cambridge College's geology department, Boston, (later Harvard University).

Having completed an apprenticeship to the Yorkshire apothecary, Lettsom came to London in 1766, where with Dr John Fothergill's help he began his training at St Thomas's Hospital. His studies were interrupted by the death of his father, which caused him to return to Van Dyke where he inherited only some slaves, whom he quickly freed, leaving himself penniless. He set up practice in nearby Tortola and was so successful that he returned to Britain to study further with Dr Cullen, a renowned physician in Edinburgh.

He extended his studies at Paris and Leyden, obtaining the MD at Leyden in June 1769. He returned to London, again with generous patronage from Dr Fothergill, and was admitted Licentiate of the College of Physicians on 25th June 1770, and more notably, Fellow of the Royal Society in 1773. The Society of Friends warmly supported his interests and practice. He married a wealthy lady and ran a thriving medical practice. He became a Fellow of the Royal College of Physicians of Edinburgh, FRSE, and Fellow of the Linnaean Society. Lettsom was a founder member of the Royal Humane Society in 1774, became a pillar of the Royal Jennerian Society and supported the Society for the Relief of Widows and Orphans of Medical Men, the Society for the Relief of Debtors, and the Philanthropic Society. These many enterprises tell both of his dedication and remarkable energy.

He wrote many papers, most importantly *Hints designed to promote beneficence, temperance and medical science*, revealing his Quaker sentiments; and Reflections *on the General Treatment and Cure of Fevers*, 1772; *The Natural History of the Tea-tree with Observations on the Medical Qualities of Tea and the effects of Tea drink-*

---

* Lettsom wrote the biography: "The Life and Works of John Fothergill M.D., 3 vols, London 1784.

ing, London 1772 (an enlarged version of his Leyden MD). He sent the first smallpox vaccine to America, to Dr Benjamin Waterhouse, Professor of Medicine in the University of Cambridge, Massachusetts, whence it spread throughout the USA.

One of his lasting legacies to the medical world was his founding of *The Medical Society of London* in 1773 to encourage informative discussions between physicians, surgeons, and apothecaries.[26] The first meeting was held on 19 May 1773. The founder members were Dr Nathaniel Hulme (physician), Dr J C Lettsom (physician to several dispensaries), Dr Joseph Hooper (accoucheur) Joseph Shaw (surgeon), Dr Charles Combe (obstetrician), William French (surgeon), Edward Ford (surgeon), Timothy Lane and William Atkinson (apothecaries), and George Vaux (surgeon).

The Society flourished and remains active to this day. Originally constituted for 30 physicians, 30 surgeons, and 30 apothecaries, its membership grew quickly. Situated at Lettsom House, Chandos Street, behind Cavendish Square, it is the oldest medical society in England. The Lettsomian Lecture was established in 1850 in his memory.

Lettsom's Quaker traditions show plainly in his many acts of charity and support of the downtrodden and impoverished. He was author of "Hints", pamphlets, diatribes, and letters that promoted Sunday schools, female industry, provisions for the blind, a bee society, soup kitchens, the mangel-wurzel, and condemnations of quackery, card parties, and intemperance. In the diversity of his interests, he has been compared to Sir Hans Sloane: a 'Renaissance Man'. He died at home, Sambrook Court, Basinghall Street on 1st Nov 1815, and was buried at the Friends' burial ground, Little Coleman Street, Bunhill Row.

CHAPTER 10

Caspar Wistar MD (1761-1818)
Physician and Anatomist; President of the American Philosophical Society; President of the Society for the Abolition of Slavery

THOUGH AMERICAN by birth, Wistar's claim for association with British Medicine lies in his training in Edinburgh where he studied to obtain his Doctorate in Medicine – MD. Wistar (Fig. 15) was born in Philadelphia, son of the Quaker, Richard Wistar and Mary Waln and grandson of Caspar Wistar, a German immigrant, Quaker and glassmaker. Born in 1761 Wistar was inspired

Fig. 15. *Caspar Wistar.*

to become a doctor at the age of 16 when he attended the wounded during the War for Independence at the Battle of Germantown.

Classically educated at the Friends School at Fourth and Walnut Streets, Philadelphia, in 1779 he entered the University of Pennsylvania, graduating in 1782 with an examination reputed to be one of the best ever at the University.[27] Wistar came to Britain, to study anatomy with John Hunter in London and then attended the Edinburgh medical school where his academic performance was outstanding. His fellow students elected him President of the Royal Medical Society and the Edinburgh Natural History Society.

He retuned to Philadelphia to practise in 1787 and established a reputation for his physicianly skills. At the same time he taught at the University of Pennsylvania and made a set of anatomical models, pathological specimens preserved by injecting them with wax – as a new aid in teaching anatomy. He later published *A System of Anatomy* in two volumes from 1811-1814, said to be the first American textbook of anatomy.

He married Isabella Marshall in 1788, but sadly, she died two years later. In 1798, he remarried, Elizabeth Mifflin, and soon they were regularly entertaining on Sunday evenings at their home at Fourth & Prune (today's Locust) Streets – famed as the 'Wistar parties'. He was a famously good host, inviting members of the American Philosophical Society as well as celebrated visitors to their home. Guests described the evenings as intellectual banquets.

In 1787 he was elected to the College of Physicians and was appointed Physician to the Philadelphia Dispensary and in 1793 was made Physician to the Pennsylvania Hospital. During the yellow fever epidemic of 1793, Wistar joined Benjamin Rush to treat patients. Wistar himself succumbed to the disease but recovered. However, his friendship with Rush cooled after he criticised Rush's use of bleeding and purging as a treatment. He was an early promoter of vaccination. Wistar was a Professor of Chemistry in the Medical Department of the College of Philadelphia from 1788 until the 1791 union of the College with the State University to form the University of Pennsylvania. He became adjunct Professor of anatomy, midwifery and surgery. After William Shippen's death in 1808, he replaced him as Professor of Anatomy. Large models and drawings enlivened his popular teachings on Medicine, Physiology and Chemistry (Fig. 16).

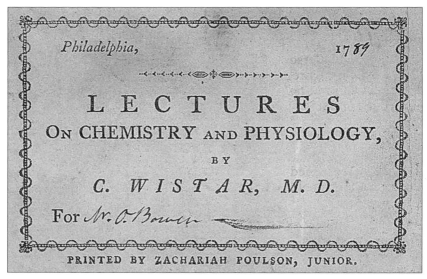

Fig. 16. *Wistar: Lecture.*

Outside his medical activities, Wistar was a member and President of both the American Philosophical Society and the Society for the Abolition of Slavery. His Quaker heritage may be seen in his involvement with the Pennsylvania Prison Society, the Humane Society, and the Society for Circulating the Benefit of Vaccination. Politically, he was a Jefferson man, a Democrat rather than a Federalist, but despite attempted persuasion by Philadelphia Democrats, he refused to run for office.

Wistar was a trustee of the College of Philadelphia from 1789-1791. After the formation of the University of Pennsylvania, he served only as a faculty member, not as a trustee. At Penn, his name lives on in the Wistar Institute, which was founded by his great-nephew Isaac Jones Wistar in 1892 based on Wistar's private collection of anatomical specimens. Today, The Wistar Institute Museum owns the only extant examples of Benjamin Rush's anatomical models. It is a flourishing centre for biomedical research. *Wistar rats,* widely used in medical research, are a strain of albino rats of the species *Rattus norvegicus,* developed at the Wistar Institute in 1906, after Caspar's death.

Wistar and Thomas Jefferson were friends and worked together on many projects, not least the collection and identification of the bones of the *Megalonyx Jeffersonii*, a giant sloth, named by Wistar. He succeeded Jefferson as President of the American Philosophical Society. He appointed a young physician, Dr. William Edmonds Horner, two years before Wistar's death in 1818, as caretaker of his museum. After he died Horner expanded this important anatomical collection. The combined collections became known as the Wistar and Horner Museum.

The popular, beautiful, leguminous climbing shrub, misnamed *Wisteria*, was named after Wistar by his admiring friend, the botanist, Thomas Nuttall in 1819.

CHAPTER 11

Joseph Jackson Lister FRS (1786-1869)
Microscopist

JOSEPH JACKSON Lister's claims to fame lie in his often forgotten development of the early microscope and in his fathering one of the greatest pioneers of surgery. The deserved fame of his son, Joseph has overshadowed his own important discoveries. Lister senior, was born in London, son of Mary and John Lister, who were observant Quakers. John was a freeman of the Bakers' company.

Joseph was educated at three different Quaker schools, Hitchin, Rochester, and Compton in Somerset, He worked with his father in a thriving wine business in Lothbury in the city of London. On a visit to the Quaker Ackworth School, he met Isabella Harris, a teacher, whom he married in 1818 and moved south. They bought Upton House in 1825, a grand old Queen Anne house in Essex.

Joseph was an amateur microscopist, whose discoveries helped perfect the objective lens system of the microscope. Frustrated by the poor resolution of existing instruments, he designed and made achromatic lenses of crown and flint glasses of different dispersion, which minimised chromatic aberration. This produced a far superior optical microscope. He performed this work in his spare time, whilst still at work as a wine merchant. He was made a Fellow of the Royal Society in 1832 in recognition of his discoveries and work on lenses and microscopes. Using his new lenses, Lister was the first to accurately show the morphology of the red blood cell in mammalian blood. When one considers the primitive state of the microscope before his times, and the importance of this instrument throughout the realms of scientific investigation, the fruits of Joseph Jackson Lister's work are of uncommon merit.

He died in October 1869 at Upton House, and was buried along with Isabella his wife, in the Friends' Burial Ground, Stoke Newington, Middlesex.

Photographs show him as a man of strikingly handsome appearance. He was the father of the celebrated Joseph Lister the surgeon and founder of antiseptic surgery. (qv).

CHAPTER 12

The Tuke family
Philanthropists; founders of the York Retreat

PHILIPPE PINEL in France, and the Quaker Tuke family in England, were independently involved in establishing humane treatment for the mentally ill. Pinel, in 1801, had written *Treatise on insanity*,[28] a revolutionary recipe for more gentle, humane treatment and abolition of widespread brutality of the mentally ill. In 1797 he effectively removed the fetters from the inmates in the Paris hospital of Bicètre. The 1845 *County Asylums Act* compelled every county and borough to provide asylum treatment for all its pauper lunatics. Lord Ashley told Parliament that this would "effect a cure in seventy cases out of every hundred" (Hansard 6th June 1845 column 193).

The Retreat at York (Fig. 17) was opened by the Quaker merchant William Tuke (1732-1822) in 1796, and extended by his son Henry, and grandson Samuel Tuke, who also was instrumental in founding The West Riding Lunatic Asylum at Wakefield.[29] The background was that in 1790, a woman named Hannah Mills, was put in the local asylum for treatment of the insane. She died within weeks. But a furore erupted when it became clear that her family had been prevented from visiting the asylum to establish the cause of her death, and even while she was confined they were not allowed to see her on the grounds that she was not in a suitable condition to be seen.

William Tuke, and others, were shaken by this incident and tried to persuade the York Quakers to build an establishment to care properly for their own psychiatric patients. Tuke had difficulty in raising the funds and so spent two years raising money by lectures describing the principles and benefits of the proposed

Fig. 17. *The Retreat at York. Early engraving.*

institution. The Retreat opened in 1796 as a 'Friends Institute for the mentally afflicted', which changed forever the way that mental illness was treated. This was one of the first of its kind in England, and pioneered new, more humane methods of treatment of the mentally ill. Inmates' restraints and chains were removed. When possible, they were housed in a pleasant environment, fed well and provided with therapeutic occupational tasks. The first superintendent was Timothy Maud, William Tuke's brother-in-law. William also founded Quaker public schools (including. Bootham School, York in 1823).

William Tuke was born in York, son of a Quaker family. He went into the family tea and coffee merchant business started by his aunt, Mary Tuke in 1725. It became part of Twining's tea company in the 1920s. Several members of William's remarkable family dynasty[30] continued his work. His son Henry (1755-1814) was a co-founder of the York Retreat. Henry's son Samuel (1784-1857) devoted himself to the York Retreat and was instrumental in the establishment of the West Riding Lunatic Asylum in Wakefield, run on similar lines.[31] The humane treatments used there were made more widely known by his text, *Description of the Retreat near York*. When he died he was buried in the hospital's grounds. Samuel's son James Hack Tuke (1819-1896), in his turn aided in its management but is mainly known for his work in Ireland in relieving poverty and the hardships of the potato famine. James's brother was Dr Daniel Hack Tuke.

Daniel Hack Tuke MD, LLD, FRCP (1827-1895)

Daniel Tuke (Fig. 18) was undoubtedly the member of his family who made the largest impression on the medical world. He was educated at the Friends' School at Tottenham.* After a brief dalliance with Law, he began to study Medicine at St Bartholomew's Hospital, London in 1849, graduating MRCS (Member of the Royal College of Surgeons) in 1852, and obtained the M.D. Heidelberg a year later. He married Esther Maria Stickney in 1853. On his honeymoon he visited the mental hospitals in Holland, Germany and France, which shows an early dedication to his family's cause, if not a huge sense of nuptial celebration. He wrote an account of these institutions in 1854. With Esther, he had three children, the second son being Henry Scott Tuke RA.

Returning to York, he became visiting physician to the York Retreat and the York Dispensary, lecturing to the York School of Medicine on psychological diseases. In 1859, he became ill, coughing blood,** and was compelled to defer plans to turn the family home into a mental hospital. He sought warmer climes for his health, but returned to England to Falmouth for prolonged rest. Then in 1874 he took a house in London's Charlotte Street, and built a psychiatric practice which grew so that in 1885 he moved to Welbeck Street. Influential at home and on the continent, he was admired and respected. Tuke was a governor of the Bethlem Hospital, and joint editor of the Journal of *Mental Science*. He was regarded as the central figure of the Medico-Psychological Association of Great Britain.

His Lancet Obituary (March 16th, 1895, 718-9) describes his steady, persistent observation with methodical recording and arranging of facts, as his chief power, for, though not ... without poetical feeling and sentiment, yet he was not imaginative, and he was rather a receiver and a recorder than an originator. He died of

---

* In 1751, the Quaker teacher Josiah Forster (1693-1763) bought a large mansion on the north side of Tottenham Green, Reynardson House. Forster's School was a boarding school for boys that he opened in 1752. The spacious house stood in 30 acres. Forster's School attracted Quakers from all over the country.
** This was probably the onset of pulmonary tuberculosis, though his subsequent health suggests it remained quiescent for long periods.

apoplexy (cerebral haemorrhage) on 5th March 1895 and was buried at the Quaker Burial Ground, Saffron Walden.

In 1858, with JC Bucknill, he had published *a Manual of Psychological Medicine,* which was widely accepted as a standard work on lunacy. Other works included *Illustrations of the Influence of the Mind on the Body* (1872); *Insanity in Ancient and Modern Life* (1878); *History of the Insane in the British Isles* (1882); and *Sleepwalking and Hypnotism* (1884). His magnum opus was a *Dictionary of Psychological Medicine* in two large volumes, 1892, which encompassed much of psychiatric practice in Britain and Europe. Another obituary notice[32] praised his geniality and kindness:

"Probably no name is so well known among alienists the world over as that of Dr. Hack Tuke. In America he had long been recognised as the British leader, and his personal friendship with most of the leading physicians practising in psychiatry was universal....

"He was an absolutely honest worker, a man with enthusiasm, energy, kindliness, and with the deepest feeling of his responsibility to humanity in regard to his professional work. He leaves behind him the feeling of having done a splendid life's work, and leaving a gap which at present seems impossible to be filled."

Fig. 18. *Daniel Hack Tuke.*

51

CHAPTER 13

Joseph Hodgson FRCS, FRS (1788-1869)

Versatile surgeon who founded the Birmingham
Eye Hospital; aortic aneurysm syndromes

BORN AT PENRITH, Cumberland, the son of a Birmingham merchant, Joseph Hodgson was educated at King Edward VI Grammar School and was apprenticed to George Freer, who was Surgeon to the Birmingham General Hospital. He was a well-known Quaker.[33] He started training at St. Bartholomew's Hospital, and in 1811 gained the Jacksonian Prize for his essay on "Wounds and Diseases of the Arteries and Veins". It was expanded and was published in 1815 with a quarto volume of illustrative engravings from drawings made by the author. It was highly thought of and translated into French. He practised at King Street, Cheapside, but made little money and returned to Birmingham in 1818 and was elected Surgeon to the Birmingham General Hospital in 1821, where he built a good practice. He described an aneurysmal dilatation [balloon-like swelling] of the proximal part of the aorta, often accompanied by dilatation or hypertrophy [overgrowth] of the heart, which was known as *Hodgson's disease.*

In 1824 he established an Eye Infirmary in Birmingham. And was for four years its only surgeon. He was invited in 1840 to become Surgeon to the Middlesex Hospital and Professor of Surgery at King's College, but declined both offers. In December, 1843 he became FRCS, one of the original 300 Fellows of the Royal College of Surgeons.* His patients included Sir Robert Peel and his family. In 1850 he was in personal attendance when the Prime

Minister, who had just resigned his office, fell from his horse in Constitution Hill and received the injury that proved fatal. Hodgson resigned from Birmingham in 1848, and the Governors presented him with his portrait, which now hangs in the Committee Room. It was not until 1849, after having made a considerable fortune in Birmingham that he returned to Westbourne Terrace, Hyde Park, London.

Hodgson was a good teacher, reputed to be an excellent diagnostician, though somewhat cautious in his prognoses. He was the second surgeon from the provinces to be elected to the Council of the Royal College of Surgeons in 1849, becoming Vice-President in 1862 and 1863; and President, 1864. He delivered the Hunterian Oration in 1855. Supported by Astley Cooper, Charles Bell and others, he was admitted F.R.S. on April 14th, 1831. He became President of the Medico-Chirurgical Society in 1851. Sir William Bowman – after whom a membrane in the eye, and the microscopic capsule of the kidney's glomeruli are named – was one of many gifted pupils whom he taught and influenced.

Little is written about his personal life. He died on February 7th, 1869, twenty-four hours after his wife, and left one daughter. He is buried at Highgate Cemetery, London.

---

* In 1745 the Guild of Surgeons, part of the Company of Barber-Surgeons separated to form the Company of Surgeons. Under Royal Charter of 1800 the Company became the Royal College of Surgeons in London. Another Charter in 1843 granted the present title: the Royal College of Surgeons of England.

CHAPTER 14

Thomas Hodgkin MD (1798-1866)
Lymphoma (Hodgkin's disease); anthropology; anti-slavery movement

ON JANUARY 10th, 1832, the 34-year-old Thomas Hodgkin took a paper he had written to the Medical and Surgical Society in London. Since he wasn't a member, the Society's secretary had to read it for him. Only eight members were present to hear his *Some Morbid Appearances of the Absorbent Glands and Spleen,* an account of six patients, severely ill with swollen lymph glands and anaemia.[34]

Fig. 19. *Thomas Hodgkin.*

He recognized that tuberculosis coexisted in some of these patients, but the firmness and size of the glands made him conclude that these findings were different. His patients' disease, a form of cancer of the lymph glands and other organs, spread to contiguous lymph node groups in an orderly manner and enlargement of the spleen was a late development. The disease was not generally recognised despite his excellent account until Sir Samuel Wilks described further cases in 1856[35] and named the disease *Hodgkin's lymphoma*, after him in 1865.

Thomas Hodgkin (Fig. 19) (1798-1866)[36] was born August 17, 1798, in Tottenham, St. James Parish, Middlesex, of a Quaker family* and studied Medicine at Edinburgh and in Paris. In France he encountered the newly-invented stethoscope of René Laennec, the use of which he advocated in a paper to the Guy's Hospital Physical Society in 1822; but he was disappointed that initially it was greeted with scepticism. From 1825 he held the post of Curator of the Museum at Guy's Hospital Medical School and Demonstrator of Morbid Anatomy, making notable advances in this subject.[37]

Hodgkin's years at Guy's Hospital were remarkably productive. He performed hundreds of autopsies and catalogued over 3000 specimens in 'the Green Book'. He gave students a systematic series of lectures on pathology and published a two-volume monograph. He described aortic regurgitation [a leaking aortic valve often caused by rheumatic fever] five years before Corrigan. Hodgkin, Richard Bright,[38] and Thomas Addison[39] were contemporaries and became known as 'the three great men of Guy's'. All three correlated clinical with postmortem findings and all had diseases named after them.

Hodgkin held radical liberal views.[40] He promoted the education of working-class men[41] and became a founding member of the Senate of the University of London in 1836. In the same year he was offered Fellowship of the Royal College of Physicians (FRCP) but declined because only two years earlier, the college had repealed its bylaw that limited the Fellowship to graduates of Oxford and

* Wellcome Collection, Archived items of correspondence, diaries, notes and drafts from the personal papers of members of the Hodgkin and Howard families Ref: PP/HO: Hodgkin family.

55

Cambridge. Hodgkin felt that he would be singled out as an exception that was unfair to other physicians. He was also aware that John Fothergill, an eminent Quaker physician, who also received his medical degree from Edinburgh, had been recommended by the President of the London Royal College of Physicians but rejected by the Fellows.

His concern about the effects of colonisation on indigenous cultures led one day to his arriving at Guy's in a carriage 'with a half naked native American', much to the displeasure of Benjamin Harrison, Treasurer of Guy's. It was perhaps because of this incident in 1837 and his plain, austere, Quaker manner of dress and his refusal of the FRCP, that Hodgkin failed to win an appointment to the permanent clinical staff of Guy's in 1837, to which Benjamin Babington was elected. Almost immediately Hodgkin left Guy's hospital, moving to St. Thomas's. Ironically, the Hodgkin Building at the Guy's Campus perpetuates his name. Hodgkin suffered other disappointments. He was not allowed to marry his true love, Sarah Godlee, because of the Quaker rule prohibiting marriage between first cousins. Even though he twice petitioned the Society of Friends to make an exception, he was refused. Later that rule was repealed. He finally married Sara Scaife, a widow but not a Quaker, in 1849.

Hodgkin devoted much of his time to the medical problems of the poor and underprivileged in England, but also to the plight of the American Indians and African natives. He published his Essay on medical education in 1828, and Lectures on the means of promoting and preserving health, London, 1835. He was active in the British and Foreign Aborigines Protection Society, which in 1909 merged with The British and Foreign Anti-Slavery Society. In later years he engaged in philosophical, geographical, and ethnographical studies. He was active in the Royal Geographical Society and in the establishment of the Ethnological Society.[42]

In 1823, the year he qualified, he met Moses Montefiore(1784-1885), a wealthy financier and philanthropist who became his lifelong patient and close friend. The relationship between the Quaker Hodgkin and the Orthodox Jew, Montefiore, was founded not only on respect for each other's professional skills, but also, perhaps, on a deeper sympathetic recognition of the issues that beset their own communities. Amalie and Edward Kass observed: "Both understood the difficulties associated with perpetuating their beliefs and maintaining their integrity when surrounded by an overwhelming majority".[43] During the last years of his life Hodgkin spent much time with Montefiore. The two friends frequently visited the Near East. Hodgkin last travelled to Israel with Sir Moses in the autumn of 1866. Before embarking on the journey Hodgkin's health had deteriorated, and he was unable to journey to Jerusalem, spending his last days in the care of a British diplomat in Jaffa. Thomas Hodgkin died on April 5, 1866, and was buried in a small protestant churchyard in Jaffa. Sir Moses carried the costs of erecting an obelisk by his grave, which carried the inscription:

"Here rests the body of Thomas Hodgkin M.D. of Bedford Square, London. A man distinguished alike for scientific attainments, medical skills and self-sacrificing philanthropy".

The graveyard, which included no more than half a dozen graves had two imposing tombstones, both now overgrown with weeds: one of a British General, the other of Hodgkin.

His grave has subsequently become forgotten and overgrown, but his medical achievements will endure. One may wonder what this man might have achieved if he, and not Benjamin Babington, had been appointed to the position of physician to Guy's Hospital. A fitting if sentimental epithet – *"medical immortal and uncompromising idealist."* – is provided by MJ Stone in an excellent biographical essay.[44] A London Blue Plaque (Fig. 20) marks his home in Bedford Square, later occupied by Thomas Wakley, founder editor of The Lancet.

Fig. 20. *Hodgkin blue plaque, Bedford Square.*

CHAPTER 15

Elizabeth Blackwell MD (1821-1910)
First female American/English doctor;
pioneer physician and campaigner

ELIZABETH BLACKWELL (Fig. 21) was born to a practising Quaker family on February 3, 1821, in an old gabled house at Counterslip, near Bristol. Her father, Samuel Blackwell, a sugar refiner, was well known in England in the 1820s for his opposition to slavery and his demands for reform in church and government. Her brother Henry was a spirited abolitionist and worker for women's suffrage. Her younger sister Emily, became America's second female physician. When the family's sugar refinery burned

Fig. 21. *Elizabeth Blackwell. US stamp.*

down, and the family faced harsh antagonism for their liberal views, in 1832 they moved to New York and six years later to Cincinnati.[45] There, Elizabeth displayed unusual academic talents. When her father died, almost penniless, she earned her living by teaching in Cincinnati and in nearby Henderson, Kentucky. Her interest in Medicine began when she attended a friend Mary Donaldson who was ill with cancer. The sick woman, impressed by her intelligence and kindness, told her to study Medicine. But the known impossibility for women to gain admission to Medical Schools at first deterred her. In 1846 she wrote in her diary:

> I felt more determined than ever to become a physician, and thus place a strong barrier between me and all ordinary marriage. I must have something to engross my thoughts...

Short of money, she worked as a teacher in North Carolina and then in Charleston, South Carolina. In 1847 she started to make applications to US schools of Medicine; no less than 19 of them rejected her. At the end of her tether she applied to Geneva College (now Hobart College), a little-known institution in west-central New York State. A Dr. Warrington sent a letter of support to the Dean who, influenced by the student vote on the dilemma, and after much deliberation, accepted her, observing:

> "This step might prove quite a good advertisement for the college."

Her student career was beset by hostility from certain students and teachers alike. Her delicate, gentlewomanly constitution aggravated her disquieting anxieties when like other medical students she was confronted with dissections, and other gruesome experiences. But courageously, she persevered, and graduated on January 23, 1849, an event, which caught the public's attention. Punch magazine noted:

> Young ladies all, of every clime,
> Especially of Britain,
> Who wholly occupy your time
> In novels or in knitting,
> Whose highest skill is but to play,
> Sing, dance, or French to clack well,
> Reflect on the example, pray,
> Of excellent Miss Blackwell!

Unable to get work in the USA she went to Paris and enrolled as a student nurse in an obstetrical hospital, La Maternité. Whilst syringing the eye of one of her patients for a virulent infection (purulent ophthalmia), some of the water had spurted into her own eye causing a suppurating infection of her left eye; she lost sight in both. Eventually a surgeon had to remove her left eye, and sight slowly returned to the other.

She had, despite her humble origins many famous and distinguished acquaintances. Visiting London, she met the ever humane, celebrated surgeon, Mr. (later Sir James) Paget (1814-1899), who helped her to gain an unprecedented entry into St. Bartholomew's Hospital in 1850.

Later in 1851 she returned to America, but still failed to obtain a hospital post. She was forced to rent a room at 44 University Place, in Jersey City, and very slowly her practice developed. In 1857 Elizabeth along with her sister Emily and Dr. Marie Zakrzewska, founded the New York Infirmary for Indigent Women and Children, where she was Professor of Hygiene. Fire again played its hand when it was burned down. After the Civil War, in 1868, she established a Women's Medical College at the Infirmary for women doctors.

In 1869 she left her sister Emily in charge of the College and returned to England where she practised. With Florence Nightingale, she opened the Women's Medical College. She lectured at the new London School of Medicine for Women and accepted a Chair in gynaecology. She was also the first female physician and doctor named in 1859 in the UK Medical Register. She retired a year later. In retirement, Elizabeth remained active in the Women's Rights Movement and was a popular lecturer; she published after some difficulties, *Counsel to Parents on the Moral Education of their Children*. She never married but adopted an orphan girl of six, Katherine Barry. The two forged an excellent relationship and Kitty was devoted to her to the end of her days. Scorned and ridiculed in the United States, Blackwell had found opportunities and success in England. Her book, *Opening the medical profession to women: autobiographical sketches** provides a revealing appraisal. She died in Hastings, on May 31, 1910.

---

* reprinted as paperback by Kessinger Publishing Company, June 2007.

Elizabeth Garrett Anderson

Blackwell's life's struggles and work are similar to those of Elizabeth Garrett Anderson. Blackwell's influence in British Medicine is illustrated by her meeting in 1859, with Elizabeth Garrett, who was facing similar difficulties.[46] As a consequence, Elizabeth Garrett decided to become a doctor.[47] British University medical schools had rejected her until finally by passing the Licentiate examination of the Society of Apothecaries she became the first woman doctor qualified in Britain. Similarly, Blackwell became the English woman graduate listed in the Medical Register. She broke through seemingly impregnable barriers of male prejudice to gain recognition and eventual fame in her profession and was a founder of women's hospitals. In 1871 Elizabeth Garrett married James G.S. Anderson, a London ship owner, but continued to advance in medical practice. In 1866 she established a dispensary for women in London (later renamed the Elizabeth Garrett Anderson Hospital, Euston Road (Fig. 22)).

Fittingly, it was Elizabeth Blackwell who was appointed Professor of Gynaecology.

Fig. 22. *Elizabeth Garrett Anderson Hospital.*

CHAPTER 16

Joseph Lister FRCS, OM, PRS, Baron Lister of Lyme Regis (1827-1912)

Surgeon; initiated antiseptic and aseptic surgery

JOSEPH LISTER[48] (Fig. 23) was born to a well-known and gifted Quaker family at Upton House, Essex, son of Joseph Jackson and Isabella Lister (see above). He attended two private schools, first in Hitchin, and the second at Grove House, Tottenham where he was academically bright, and 'full of spirit', according to his teachers. He showed an interest in natural history and human bones.

Fig. 23. *Joseph Lister.*

Lister's elevated place in the history of Medicine rests on his invention of techniques to eradicate or prevent infections, particularly of surgical wounds. He read Medicine at University College, graduating in 1852, and unusually quickly was elected a Fellow of the Royal College of Surgeons in the same year. As a student, he had watched surgery performed by Robert Liston (1794-1847), renowned as the most rapid amputator of his day. Rapidity was important because it was known that the risk of life-threatening wound infection was greater when operations took a long time, and because rapid surgery before anaesthesia was available reduced the duration of the patients' terrible pain. He also studied histology under William Sharpey. Using one of his father's newly developed microscopes (see above). He wrote an important paper on the "Use of the Microscope in Medicine". But Lister wanted to become a surgeon. In 1856 he was elected assistant surgeon to James Syme at the Edinburgh Royal Infirmary, and married his daughter, Agnes. They rented a house at No 11 Rutland Street. The engagement led him to resign his membership of the Society of Friends and to become a Scottish Episcopalian, though he retained to the end of his life nearly all his Quaker characteristics. He continued to hone his surgical skills. He developed new techniques and equipment. His research in physiology as it related to surgery flourished; he gave lectures and published papers on inflammation and blood clotting.

Lister became Regius Professor of surgery at the University of Glasgow on January 28th, 1860. He gave a course of lectures to a class of 182 students but had no charge of beds until Aug 15th, 1861 – nineteen months after his appointment to the Chair of Surgery when he was elected Surgeon to the Royal Infirmary. He now began to investigate antiseptic treatment of compound fractures, abscesses, and surgical wounds.

As a surgeon, Lister was concerned with the universally high mortality rate of post-amputation patients and the high rate of gangrene after surgery. However, before him, the Jew, Ignaz Philipp Semmelweis (1818-1865), a tragic Hungarian obstetrician, realized the importance of cleanliness when he observed that mothers treated during childbirth by nurses and doctors, with hands soiled by recent handling of cadavers, had a much higher mortality rate than those whom he assisted He employed chlorinated washes. Lister had not heard of Semmelweis's work until much later.

63

Antisemitism and the Hungarian revolution put an end to Semmelweis's research. To illustrate the magnitude of the problem at that time, Nuland recalls[49] that when George IV decided in 1821 that an unsightly cyst must be surgically removed from his scalp by the famous surgeon, Astley Cooper, he did not pause to consider that he would be risking his life by undergoing the simple operation, which was accompanied by a mortality rate considerably higher than that of modern, open-heart surgery.

In an 1867 article titled 'Hospitalism', Sir James Young Simpson of Edinburgh, the inventor of chloroform anaesthesia, studied the results of more than two thousand in-hospital extremity amputations in Britain, and found that 41 percent of hospital patients died. Meanwhile, in 1857, Louis Pasteur (1822-1895) had shown that fermentation [allied to pus forming infection, i.e. putrefaction] was caused by living organisms in the air, which on entering body tissues caused them to ferment.[50] Lister speculated that airborne bacteria could be the cause of infection in wounds: the '*Germ Theory*' of infection, and set about eliminating them:[51]

"But when it had been shown by the researches of Pasteur that the septic properties of the atmosphere depended not on the oxygen, or any gaseous constituent, but on minute organisms suspended in it, which owed their energy to their vitality, it occurred to me that decomposition in the injured part might be avoided without excluding the air, by applying as a dressing some material capable of destroying the life of the floating particles. Upon this principle I have based a practice of which I will now attempt to give a short account.

"The material which I have employed is carbolic or phenolic acid, a volatile organic compound, which appears to exercise a peculiarly destructive influence upon low forms of life, and hence is the most powerful antiseptic with which we are at present acquainted.

"The first class of cases to which I applied it was that of compound fractures, in which the effects of decomposition in the injured part were especially striking and pernicious. The results have been such as to establish conclusively the great principle that all local inflammatory mischief and general febrile disturbances which follow severe injuries are due to the irritating and poisonous influence of decomposing blood or sloughs.

64

Fig. 24. *Lister's carbolic spray.*

For these evils are entirely avoided by the antiseptic treatment..."[52]

From 1866 onwards, he used carbolic acid in and around surgical wounds and on surgical instruments by using an 'antiseptic' carbolic acid spray in the operating theatre (Fig. 24). He first applied this method in 1865 while treating a compound fracture of a tibia that typically carried a 60% mortality rate caused by sepsis. The procedure was successful.[53] Lister published his antiseptic method in the Lancet for January 8, 1870: before the antiseptic period he noted 16 deaths in 35 cases or 1 death in every 2½ cases, during the antiseptic period 6 deaths in 40 cases or 1 death in every 6⅔ cases.[54] Syme, and later Sir James Paget adopted Lister's antisepsis technique. Carbolic acid, especially the spray, was a strong irritant and Lister was forced to find and use more dilute antiseptics; and later used heat-sterilized instruments.

In 1869 he returned to Edinburgh following the death of Syme. Lister was appointed in his place on August 18th. Lister took a furnished house at 17 Abercromby Square, moving afterwards to

9 Charlotte Square, then a fashionable medical area. He soon was recognised as Scotland's leading surgeon, and acquired a large practice. In June 1877 however, he was appointed to the Chair at King's College London, and took a house at 12 Park Crescent, Regent's Park.

Initially Lister's antisepsis was not accepted. Curiously, opposition in England and the USA was directed more against his germ theory than against his carbolic treatment. But his consistently superior morbidity and mortality rates proved overwhelming evidence of its efficacy in reducing sepsis, gangrene, and fatal pyaemia and septicaemia (blood stream infections), then so common. Though his methods were already well founded, a dramatic instance furthered his cause. The wiring of a fractured kneecap, entailing open exposure of the area, often resulted in fatal sepsis. On October 26 1877, Lister, for the first time, carried out the operation under antiseptic conditions without ensuing infection. News of the operation was widely publicized, at first arousing much opposition. Its success persuaded surgical opinion throughout the world to accept his methods. They were rapidly adopted particularly by the Military in the Franco-Prussian war. By 1878, in Germany, Robert Koch (1843-1910), a Nobel prize winner in 1905, was using steam for sterilising surgical instruments and dressings. Avoidance of infection by using clean or sterilised instruments and dressings gradually led to 'aseptic surgery' that complemented his earlier use of 'antisepsic' carbolic acid.

The great surgeon and writer Sir George Frederick Treves (1853-1923) gave an indication of the huge significance of Lister's work:

Lister created anew the ancient art of healing; he made a reality of the hope which had for all time sustained the surgeon's endeavours; he removed the impenetrable cloud which had stood for centuries between great principles and successful practice; and he rendered possible a treatment which had hitherto been but the vision of the dreamer. The nature of his discovery – like that of most great movements – was splendid in its simplicity and magnificent in its littleness. To the surgeon's craft it was but the 'one thing needful.' With it came the promise of a wondrous future; without it was the hopelessness of an impotent past.[55]

The more modern commentary of Sherwin B. Nuland goes further, in describing Lister the man:

> There was a flavor of simple goodness in his life, flowing evenly from the philosophical spring of a distinctive faith that has nourished the spirit of more than a few of the moral leaders of the past three hundred years. The source of that spring is to be found in the ethical principles of the Religious Society of Friends.

Lister received many honours and awards. In 1897 he received the Honorary Gold Medal, the highest distinction the Royal College of Surgeons can bestow. At the Royal Society he was elected a Fellow in 1860; served on the Council from 1881-1883; he became President in succession to Lord Kelvin from 1895-1900. He delivered the Croonian Lecture in 1863, was awarded a Royal Medal in 1880, and the Copley Medal in 1900.

A dedicated surgeon, he treated both war wounds and surgical wounds; he experimented with various antiseptics, developed absorbable sutures, and introduced a method of surgical drainage. He was one of the 12 original members of the Order of Merit. His wife died in 1892 and he retired from practice the following year. He was offered the Presidency of the Royal College of Surgeons in 1885 but declined. In 1883 his outstanding works were rewarded by a baronetcy by Queen Victoria. He was thus the first British surgeon to be elevated to the peerage, and upon his death on 12th Feb 1912, from pneumonia, his remains were interred in Westminster Abbey. A blue plaque at 12 Park Crescent, W1 records: Lister, Joseph, Lord (1827-1912), Surgeon, lived here. Westminster 1915.

He was described[56] as equable in temper, he was courteous to all, but sheltered himself behind a natural reserve which many attributed to shyness. A lover of home life and very simple in his tastes, he maintained to the last, evidence of his Quaker upbringing by using 'thou' and 'thee' when writing familiarly to members of his family. He was deeply religious, but without ostentation, attaching himself to no sect, but living a Christian life. No lover of money, he proportioned his fees to what he thought a patient could afford rather than what it was right or customary to charge, and he never, therefore, acquired wealth. When he died, it was said that Lister had saved more lives than all the wars in history had claimed.

CHAPTER 17

Sir Jonathan Hutchinson FRCS, FRS (1828-1913)

Pegged teeth of congenital syphilitics –
Hutchinson's teeth; fixed dilated pupil of
temporal lobe coning – Hutchinson's pupil;
first account of cranial arteritis;[57]
Hutchinson's triad that characterises
congenital syphilis

HUTCHINSON,[58] (Fig. 25) was the second of eight sons and two daughters of Jonathan Hutchinson, a middleman in the flax trade and Elizabeth Massey. He was born on 23 July 1828, at Red House,

Fig. 25. *Sir Jonathan Hutchinson.*

Quayside, in Selby, North Yorkshire, now a mining area. Selby boasts a beautiful abbey, founded on a monastery in 1069 AD. by the monk, Benedict from Auxerre, and his successor Abbot Hugh, under the instruction of William the Conqueror.

Compared with the ultrastructured modern educational systems, it is remarkable that Hutchinson had no formal schooling but was taught by governesses at home until the age of 17. He was then apprenticed to the surgeon Caleb Williams of York in 1845. Between 1846 and 1850, Hutchinson attended the York School of Medicine, with his lifelong friend, Hughlings Jackson* and was taught by Thomas Laycock, later celebrated Professor of the practice of Physic at Edinburgh University.

He completed his studies at St. Bartholomew's Hospital, where Sir James Paget was an important influence. He qualified MRCS and LSA in 1850. From 1853 he wrote weekly hospital reports for the Medical Times and Gazette, a rival to the Lancet, remaining a prolific writer throughout his life. He wrote the ten volume Archives of Surgery (1885-99): a remarkable single-handed labour.

Hutchinson secured appointments at the Royal London Ophthalmic Hospital and the Blackfriars Hospital for Skin Diseases. After marrying Jane Pynsent West in 1856, he began private practice at 14 Finsbury Circus, London. In 1859 he was appointed assistant surgeon to the London Hospital; and in that year helped found the New Sydenham Society. He obtained the FRCS on Dec. 11th, 1862 and in 1863 was appointed full surgeon to the London Hospital. A successful practice and the insistent counsel of Paget determined his reluctant move in 1894, to Cavendish Square – haunt of the more ambitious medical consultants. In 1889 he was elected President of the Royal College of Surgeons. The breadth of his expertise is astonishing. In his day he was accepted as a leading authority on ophthalmology, dermatology, neurology, and in particular syphilis.

His "amazingly retentive memory, coupled with his genius for teaching, enabled him to fascinate large audiences on a multiplicity of subjects. He attained a unique status. With his tall, stooping frame, his untidy black beard and his slow speech he

---

* Jackson was the most original and most brilliant British neurologist of the 19th century.

presented an austere, seemingly humourless figure. It might seem amazing that such a solemn man could enthral his audiences but this is precisely what he did."[59]

Sir Rickman Godlee (the first English surgeon to remove a brain tumour,[60] and author of Lord Lister's biography) recalls a letter[61] sent to him in September 1922 by his colleague, the great Sir Frederick Treves (of Elephant Man fame):

"Hutchinson was, without question, a great teacher. He attracted, I believe, a larger number of students to his demonstrations than did any other surgeon of his time in London. He had indeed a great following. He was an admirable speaker. He was not eloquent, nor did he make a practice of rhetoric, but adopted a slow, quiet, solemn and modest manner which was very impressive and effective. He made his teaching interesting by the ingenuity of his arguments, by apt illustrations and vivid metaphors and by an occasional quaintness of expression which impressed the memory. Above all were a solemness and simplicity of utterance which was almost monastic. I think a prominent fault of his was a tendency to make facts accord with theory – and he had many theories. His theories about leprosy* also pressed to a position far beyond that supported by fact."

Hutchinson became FRS in 1882. His fame earned him honorary degrees from the Universities of Glasgow, Cambridge, Edinburgh, Oxford, Dublin and Leeds. He was knighted in 1908.

He wrote many papers. I would fail to give adequate credit without mentioning some which have withstood the test of time. They subsumed accounts of: the pegged lateral incisors and notched short, central upper incisor teeth of congenital syphilitics – known as Hutchinson's teeth; numerous skin disorders; choroido-retinal lesions; the fixed dilated pupil of temporal lobe coning : Hutchinson's pupil; and he probably gave the first account of cranial arteritis.[62] He wrote important articles on progeria; senile choroidal degeneration; Hutchinson's triad – the combination of Hutchinson's teeth,[63] interstitial keratosis, and eighth nerve deafness characterising congenital syphilis; Hutchinson's mask – facial numbness in tabes; Claude Bernard-Horner syndrome;

---

* In 1863, he propounded what he called his "fish hypothesis" – that decomposing fish is the one sole cause of leprosy. Despite Hansen's discovery of the leprosy bacillus 1874, Hutchinson adhered to his misguided hypothesis all his life.

Fig. 26. *Sir Jonathan Hutchinson's Museum at Haslemere. 78 High Street, Haslemere, Surrey, GU27 2LA.*

Hutchinson's sign – the nasociliary affection of herpes zoster (shingles); and the Klippel-Feil syndrome of congenital fused vertebrae in the neck.

Like his associate Thomas Hodgkin (1798-1866), Hutchinson was a devout Quaker, who lectured on Sunday afternoons at the Meeting House, near his home in Haslemere, Surrey. There, he built up an educational museum (see Fig. 26) and a library providing an outline of history, charts of figures tabulating events from antiquity, for the benefit of the population of the locality. The museum displayed rocks, fossils, preserved plants, and flowers, as well as freshly gathered, birds' eggs, an aviary and vivarium exhibiting natural objects of the neighbourhood, including the common viper. In 1895 the collections moved to Museum Hill and in 1926 to the High Street where it has become a popular haunt for visitors.

He published a monthly journal, which includes features of a schoolbook, encyclopaedia, and a journal of science and literature. Few doctors were more versatile.

His vast collection of specimens and watercolour drawings, he donated to the Medical Graduates' College and Polyclinic at 22 Chenies Street, London, founded in 1899. In the Dictionary of National Biography (1927, p.279), Jonathan Hutchinson was described as 'the greatest general practitioner in Europe.' Sir Rickman Godlee published a fine biographical essay. He related:

"We older men who remember Sir Jonathan Hutchinson well, recall a tallish dark figure that changed very little from middle life to old age; dark eyes that seemed to look past you through his spectacles; black hair, black beard lengthening and growing grey with age; a suit of black broadcloth and a top hat that grudgingly gave place to a wide-awake. We see him presiding at our medical meetings and addressing them in precise clear-cut sentences, rather solemn, without much sparkle, but full of meat, and made attractive by more than a trace of Yorkshire accent...."

He retired from London Hospital in 1883, and became emeritus Professor of surgery. The Hutchinson triennial prize essay was established to commemorate his services. Having become President of the Royal College of Surgeons he began the publication of his series Archives of Surgery (1889-1900), which was issued quarterly.

His wife died in 1886. He had six sons and four daughters. One son, Jonathan, became Surgeon to the London Hospital; another, Proctor, a laryngologist, died young; Roger, was in practice at Haslemere.

He died at his house, The Library, Inval, Haslemere, at the age of 84, on January 23, 1913. It was in the parish churchyard that a goodly company of friends and admirers gathered round his grave. And here, as he directed, these words are inscribed upon his tombstone:

"A Man of Hope and Forward-looking Mind."

CHAPTER 18

Rickman John Godlee KCVO, MS, FRCS (1849-1925)

Surgery of pulmonary infections; removal of first brain tumour in England; biographer of Lord Lister

RICKMAN GODLEE (Fig. 27), nephew of Lord Lister, was born on 15 February 1849, son of Quaker parents in Queen Square, London. His father, Rickman Godlee, was a barrister of the Inner Temple, his mother was Mary Lister, sister of Joseph, Lord Lister.

Fig. 27. *Sir Rickman John Godlee.*

He was educated at Mr. Abbott's school, Grove House, Tottenham, popular amongst Friends' families. He first studied and graduated in Arts, then enrolled in Medicine at University College in 1867, where he graduated M.B. and M.S., winning Gold Medals. After serving as house surgeon, in 1872 he went to live with his uncle, Joseph Lister who was then Professor of Surgery in Edinburgh. He quickly learned his novel antisepsis methods, and published his work in the Lancet (1878, i, 694, 729) with the title, "The Antiseptic Treatment in Edinburgh".

On retracing his steps to London, he became Surgical Registrar at University College Hospital. His first original discovery was made whilst opening an abscess (osteomyelitic) of the tibial bone in the leg. He examined the microscopic appearances of the pus and used a camera lucida to record "certain curious minute bodies which were arranged in rows or chains". This was the first time these streptococcal bacteria had been seen in pus. Robert Koch, (the Nobel prize winning Jewish founder of bacteriology) confirmed them independently in 1881.

He was elected Assistant Surgeon to Charing Cross Hospital and Lecturer in Anatomy in the Medical School in 1876. He was then elected Assistant Surgeon and demonstrator in anatomy to University College Hospital in 1877. His anatomical work and drawings he used in an Atlas of Human Anatomy in 1876, based on more than 100 dissections. There were four parts; the full work with 48 plates appeared in 1880. Godlee inherited his uncle's artistic prowess and tastes through his mother from the Lister family.

He was appointed Surgeon to the Brompton Hospital for Diseases of the Chest in 1884, and in 1900, was made Consulting Surgeon. He began to lecture, and published several high quality papers on the surgery of chest infections. With Sir James Kingston Fowler, in 1898 he wrote the surgical parts of the book: The Diseases of the Lungs.

Godlee acted as private assistant to Lord Lister for some years; if the family ties had strained the professional relationship, it was not evident. A remarkable event occurred on 3rd November 1884. Mcewen had removed a meningioma in 1879, the first removal of a brain tumour in Britain. Godlee was called to a patient, a Mr Henderson, aged 25, diagnosed by Dr Hughes Bennett as having a tumour of the brain. He was admitted into the Hospital for Epilepsy and Paralysis, Regent's Park, and the position of the tumour was located (applying the recent experimental work of Ferrier) in the cortical substance near the upper third of the fissure of Rolando. The patient expressed a strong desire to have it removed, and Rickman Godlee was called upon to operate in the presence of Hughlings Jackson and David Ferrier. The localization proved to be accurate and the glioma (malignant tumour) was extirpated without difficulty; sadly, the patient died of secondary surgical complications. Godlee had performed the first brain tumour removal in England, if not in Britain.[64] He became full Surgeon at University College Hospital in 1885 and resigned on April 1st, 1914. He succeeded his cousin, Marcus Beck, as Professor of Clinical Surgery in 1892, and was appointed Holme Professor of Clinical Surgery in 1900 in succession to Christopher Heath (see below).

At the Royal College of Surgeons, Godlee was a Member of the Court of Examiners from 1893-1903, Bradshaw Lecturer in 1907, and Hunterian Orator in 1913. He was Vice-President, then in 1911 was elected President, re-elected in 1912 and again in 1913. He addressed the American College of Surgeons, about the history of the English College in such a spirit of brotherhood that valuable links were forged as the Great War drew near.

Godlee was President of the Royal Society of Medicine in 1916-1917. During the war he served the Central Medical War Committee. In 1920 he retired to a farm, Combe End, at Whitchurch in Oxfordshire. It overlooked the Thames and the grounds ran down to the river. Here he made many improvements and additions to the house, acted as a gentleman farmer, took part in the affairs of the village, and wrote a history of it in the Parish Magazine.

He married in 1891, Juliet Mary, daughter of Frederic Seebohm, but had no children. He died at Whitchurch on Sunday, April 18th, 1925, with the diagnosis of ruptured abdominal aneurysm. He was buried at Whitchurch. Lady Godlee survived him.

Many honours fell to Rickman Godlee. He was surgeon to the Royal Household in the time of Queen Victoria, and Surgeon in Ordinary to King Edward VII and to King George V. He was created a baronet in 1912 and was decorated K.C.V.O. in 1914. Lady Godlee presented a striking portrait in oils to the Royal College of Surgeons in 1925.

To the last, Godlee retained many traces of his Quaker ancestry. It was said of him that he was relentlessly honest, downright, and somewhat sarcastic, he took nothing for granted that was capable of demonstration. Whatever he undertook was done thoroughly, and he thus became an expert oarsman, for he loved the river; a good carpenter; an excellent farmer; and a field naturalist. His artistic tastes extended beyond drawing, for he made a fine collection of etchings, and was an expert in books, their paper and their binding. His lucid biography of Lord Lister, his uncle is the definitive work of reference. Courteous in manner and easy of address, he filled the office of President of the College with great dignity. He bequeathed large sums to University College Hospital and College.

CHAPTER 19

William Allen Sturge MVO, MD, FRCP (1850-1919)

Sturge Weber Kalischer syndrome

WILLIAM STURGE (Fig. 28) is remembered mainly for having his name appended to a rare but distinctive syndrome, (described below) well known to medical students as a 'spot diagnosis' in their examinations. In later years he became an archaeologist and collector of renown. Sturge led an interesting but turbulent life, beset by illnesses, despite which he was a successful physician.

Fig. 28. *William Allen Sturge.*

He was born in Bristol, son of a Quaker father, William Sturge, a wealthy surveyor. In 1865 he was sent to a Quaker school in London. While playing soccer there, he injured his knees, and staying with his uncle, a doctor, after this accident he became interested in Medicine, which he studied at Bristol. His student days however, were interrupted by serious illnesses, diphtheria and then rheumatic fever. He was sent abroad as a 'medical attendant' to accompany a wealthy man to Egypt. He resumed his medical studies on his return and graduated from University College, London, in 1873.

Sturge trained in Neurology as a resident medical officer and registrar at the National Hospital for Paralysis and Epilepsy, Queen Square. In 1876 he furthered his studies in Neurology with the great Jean Martin Charcot (1825-1893) in La Salpêtrière, Paris, and general pathology and Medicine with Jean Alfred Fournier (1832-1915) at the St. Louis Hospital. It was in Paris that he met a young doctor, Emily Bovell, who was one of the original half dozen women admitted to the Medical School of Edinburgh, only to be rejected by the male students and faculty. All of these women eventually completed their medical training elsewhere. William Sturge strongly supported the muted calls of the day for women to be allowed to practise Medicine. They married in September 1877 and returned to set up a practice together in Wimpole Street. He was appointed physician and pathologist to the Royal Free Hospital, and lecturer to the Women's Medical School. An excellent lecturer and teacher he built a thriving practice in both organic and psychological illnesses. But his wife fell ill and they moved to Nice in 1880 where he again started to see patients. Sturge looked after Queen Victoria and her family during her four visits to Cimez. In recognition, she awarded him the MVO (Member Victorian Order).

Emily died in 1885. A year later William married Julia Sherriff, who was his nurse in Nice. During their holiday travels he began to collect Greek vases and Palaeolithic and Neolithic flints.

He had recurrent attacks of the rheumatic fever that had marred his youth, and on this account in 1907 he ceased to practise and returned to England. He there continued to study early Greek art and was a collector of Etruscan vases. At his home, Icklingham Hall in Suffolk, he created one of the finest private museums of flint implements in the world, carefully classified and catalogued.

XXXVII.—*A Case of Partial Epilepsy, apparently due to a Lesion of one of the Vaso-motor Centres of the Brain. By W. ALLEN STURGE, M.D. Read April 18, 1879.*

ADA BROOK, æt. 6½. Both father and mother are living and healthy; both are steady; there is no blood-relationship between them. Two other children are living and healthy; three are dead, one by an accident, and the other two, who were twins, in early infancy. The mother never miscarried. The father had an uncle who is said to have died 'out of his mind;' he was not, however, in an asylum, but died in his own house. There is no other history of insanity, and no history of fits in the family. Several members of the father's family are said to have died of consumption.

Fig. 29. *Sturge's paper: title page.*

His collection of more than 100,000 pieces is now in the British Museum. His collection of Greek amphora is housed in the Toronto Museum, Canada as the Sturge Collection.

In the winter of 1918 he suffered from influenza and then nephritis. He died, childless, in March 1919.

Sturge's name has been perpetuated[65] as the first physician to describe the 'Sturge Weber Kalischer syndrome' syndrome in 1879 in a 6½ year-old girl. This is a blood vessel malformation (angioma) visible on one side of the face, and present also on the brain's surface where it causes epilepsy, weakness of the limbs and sometimes haemorrhage. Sturge described (Fig. 29) with great precision:

"She started to have twitching on left side of her body as a six months old baby [focal epilepsy]. The attacks worsened but without loss of consciousness. Later, the twitching started to spread to the other side and she would lose consciousness [generalised epilepsy]. She benefited from potassium bromide. Of particular interest was that the child had what was described as "mother's mark" on the right side of the head and face. The skin [blood vessel] lesion was accurately demarcated in the midline and involved the upper lip, nose, forehead, scalp, and back of the neck extending a little beyond the midline on the chin and on the upper part of the sternum. It extended as low as the third or fourth dorsal vertebra.

The lips, gums, tongue, roof of mouth, floor of mouth, uvula, and pharynx were all similarly affected. The right eye was larger (buphthalmos & congenital glaucoma) and the sclera, choroid and retina were all affected by a vascular malformation. In addition there was a patch about the size of the palm of the hand over the left eye, frontal and temporal regions. The mark was of a deep purple colour, the colour partially disappearing on firm pressure. The affected parts were distinctly larger than the corresponding parts on the other side."

This mark, Sturge called a "port-wine" stain.[66]

Sturge presented his case to the Clinical Society in London on 18th April 1879. He deduced that the brain lesion was a surface malformation of blood vessels similar to that he had observed on the skin. His colleagues doubted this suggestion of a lesion on the surface of the brain, but not of the deeper brain substance, because he argued, such pathology would have caused epilepsy from the outset. Sturge's speculation proved correct. But, it was not until 1901 that Siegfried Kalischer (1862-?) provided pathological proof;

Fig. 30. *Case of Sturge Weber syndrome.*

and, Parkes Weber (1863-1962) in 1922 demonstrated the intracranial calcifications in the surface blood vessel malformation (angioma) in a typical case. Fig. 30 shows a typical example, recently observed.

William Sturge was described by his distinguished obituarist, Sir Thomas Barlow, Bt, KCVO, FRS, PRCP (1845-1945) as

"a close and accurate observer, keen in reasoning and original in speculation....

He had the gift of fluent and luminous exposition... Sturge was exceedingly humane. From his studentship, onwards he took the deepest interest in the welfare of his patients. He never spared his efforts, especially for poor chronic nervous cases, to make the best of their condition, and he was so well read and wide in his intellectual sympathies that it was no wonder that many educated men and women found in him a tower of strength..."[67]

CHAPTER 20

Sir Henry Head MD, FRCP, FRS (1861-1940)

Sensory nerves; dermatomes; aphasia

HENRY HEAD (Fig. 31) was born of Quaker stock on 4 Aug 1861 at 6 Park Road, Stoke Newington, son of an insurance broker at Lloyds. Educated at Charterhouse and Trinity College, Cambridge (1st class Honours in both parts of Natural Science Tripos), he chose to study Medicine, influenced by his mother's cousin, Marcus Beck, who had been Joseph Lister's assistant. For a period after

Fig. 31. *Sir Henry Head (1895).*

Cambridge, he worked with Hering on respiratory physiology in Prague, acquiring fluency in both French and German. Hering was famous for the Hering-Breuer reflex, whereby passive inflation of the lungs causes reflex prolongation of expiration, mediated by the Vagus nerve. It was described in 1868, and is important in the control of breathing. Head returned to University College Hospital, qualifying in 1890. He worked at Queen Square under Thomas Buzzard, and at Victoria Park Hospital for Chest Diseases, where he developed his interests in pain and in physiology.[68] His Cambridge MD thesis 'On disturbances of sensation with especial reference to the pain of visceral disease', was later published in *Brain* (1893). It was of outstanding merit.

In 1903, with the assistance of Sherren and Rivers, he made many observations on himself after sectioning the superficial ramus (branch) of his own radial nerve at the wrist. He undertook this experiment because of his annoyance with the unreliability of patients as sensory witnesses.[69] The results were first published in *Brain* in 1908 and were widely acclaimed for their clarification of the normal anatomy of the sensory nerves, vital in clinical examination.

Patterns and the referral of pain led him to study herpes zoster (shingles) with A. W. Campbell, pathologist to Rainhill County Asylum.[70] From this his investigations of the dermatomes (areas of skin supplied by a single nerve root) naturally evolved. He therefore investigated shingles that was then common in his patients afflicted by syphilitic brain disease (GPI). His enthusiasm forced him to live in the hospital for two years recording 450 cases and 21 autopsy studies. Foerster observed the remarkable accuracy of Head's observations when compared with the method of section of nerve roots.

He wrote an important paper with Gordon Holmes in 1911 on sensory disturbances from cerebral lesions. His last major work, *Aphasia and Kindred Disorders of Speech*, appeared in two volumes in 1926, lauded by Critchley as "the finest monograph on the subject of aphasia in the neurological literature." Here, his originality brought critical definition to the then materialistic notions of what he scornfully described as the 'diagram-makers.' Describing "semantic aphasia", he provided a link between the linguistic and the intellectual aspects of speech. Although some of his opinions have been criticised, the full implications of this work have been credited and amplified by modern aphasiologists.

Head's singular merit was rewarded by his receiving: The Marshall Hall medal of the Royal Medical and Chirurgical Society in 1903, the Royal Medal of the Royal Society in 1908, and the Moxon Medal of the Royal College of Physicians in 1927.

He married Ruth Mayhew, headmistress and author, in 1904 and they worked together on her writing and on his poetry, with mutual devotion. His interest in the arts, music and humanity were wide and deep; he could discourse on topics from Goethe to Guardi or Mozart without effort. Robert Nichols wrote about him in The Times:

"He had Leonardo's lofty human compassion, humility, patience, and profound serenity of spirit."

After the onset of Parkinsonism in 1919, he retired in 1925 to live in Dorset and then Reading. Even in this period, his lively mind and indomitable enthusiasm immensely stimulated the fortunate few who were privileged to share his conversation. He courageously eschewed all drug therapy fearful that solanaceous drugs would impair his mind. He died on 9th October 1940, immobilised by illness, just able to talk, but mentally active. His fortune, he left to medical science, the Royal Society acting as legatee. In his obituary notice Sir Gordon Holmes commented:[71]

"the most lasting impression will be his enthusiasm and his vivid scientific imagination, which was always directed to elucidating the nature of normal function from the disorders produced by disease. It was in fact in arranging clinical experiments on scientific lines and in combining observations into hypotheses rather than as an astute observer that Head excelled."

CHAPTER 21

Sir George Newman MD, FRCP (1870-1948)

Chief Medical Officer to the Ministry of Health; public health reforms

NEWMAN WAS the son of Henry Stanley Newman and Mary Ann Pumphrey. His father was a Quaker who undertook several missionary journeys, including one to India, and edited *The Friend*, a Quaker journal. He was educated at Quaker schools: Sidcot School in Somerset (1881-1885) and then at Bootham School in York (1885-1887). His decision to become a doctor seems to have been in the nature of a 'religious calling' but fitted in with other ideas, and there is no doubt about his aunt's influence. At Bootham, he developed his love of writing and developed his clarity of style. Here he formed a friendship with Arnold Rowntree (1872-1951), which lasted all his life.

He studied Medicine at the University of Edinburgh and then King's College London before gaining his MD (with gold medal). He was lecturer in infectious diseases at King's, and became in 1900, Medical Officer to the Borough of Finsbury. He published *Infant Mortality: a Social Problem* in 1906, regarded as a medical classic. He was appointed Chief Medical Officer to the Board of Education 1907, and then in 1919 Chief Medical Officer to the Ministry of Health.[72] Such was the importance of his work that in 1911 he was knighted, in 1918 he was appointed KCB, Knight Commander of the Order of Bath and in 1935 appointed GBE, Knight Grand Cross of the Order of the British Empire. He received several Honorary degrees, and was made an Honorary Fellow of the Royal College of Surgeons of England, and Fellow of King's College, London.

Newman remained a devout Quaker.[73] From 1899, he was the (anonymous) editor of the Friends' Quarterly Examiner for some forty years. In 1914 he helped to found the Friends' Ambulance Unit, to provide medical aid for soldiers and civilians in war zones. When conscription was introduced in 1916 he negotiated exemptions for Quakers serving with the ambulance unit. His publications included *George Fox – The Founder of Quakerism* (1924), *Application of Quaker Principle in Medical Practice* (1930) and *Quaker Profiles* (1946). His obituary was published in the Lancet 1948; 1: 888-9.

CHAPTER 22

Sir Joseph Barcroft CBE, MA, DSc., Hon. MD, Hon. FRCOG, FRS (1872-1947)

Physiologist; respiratory function of blood; foetal physiology

'SIR JB', AS he was affectionately called[74] more than earns his place with the medical graduates for the widespread and lasting clinical impact of his work, which is mirrored in a multitude of honorary medical degrees, He was born into a Quaker family on

Fig. 32. *Sir Joseph Barcroft.*

July 26, 1872 at the Glen, Newry, County Down, Northern Ireland. His parents, Henry and Anna (née Malcolmson), were Quakers, originally from Lancashire. His father worked in textiles (linen) and became deputy lieutenant of County Down and High Sheriff of County Armagh. Joseph went to Bootham School, York, and then the Leys School, Cambridge. At an unusually early age he was awarded a BSc (London, 1891).

Barcroft (Fig. 32) gained admission to King's College Cambridge in 1894, achieving first class honours in natural sciences in 1896. Three years later he was elected a Fellow of Kings. He won the Walshingham Medal for biological research (1899), and shared the Gedge Prize for physiological research with Henry (later Sir Henry) Dale. In 1900 he was appointed lecturer in natural science at Kings, where he remained for 25 years. By the outbreak of the First World War he had achieved international recognition for his work on the Respiratory Function of Blood; a monograph with that title published in 1914 is still regarded as a classic.[75] He also invented the Barcroft differential blood gas manometer, an instrument that measured the pressures of gases in the blood. He was curious to discover how the heart and lungs functioned at high-altitudes.[76] He therefore organized expeditions to the peak of Tenerife (1910), to Monte Rosa (1911), and to the Peruvian Andes (1922) to assess the effects of altitude on the oxygen and carbon dioxide in the blood. He was a typical "guinea pig scientist," using himself as subject in his experiments, often attended by serious dangers. During the First World War, when he was called to an army Experimental Station (near Salisbury) to test asphyxiating gases, he exposed himself to the potentially lethal hydrogen cyanide. In 1920, to calculate the minimum quantity of oxygen required for human survival, he built a glass chamber and lived in it for six days. Inside the chamber, the pressure of oxygen had been dropped to 84 mm Hg. In another experiment on himself using hypothermia, he collapsed with almost fatal consequences.

Several books disclosed the extent of his fundamental researches and their applications.[77,78,79] From 1925 to 1937 he held the Chair of Physiology at Cambridge. His final research, begun in 1933, concerned foetal respiration.

Honours abounded. He received several honorary doctorates. He was President of the physiological section of the British

Association (1920), and elected Fellow of the Royal Society on 5 May 1910. He succeeded Sir Arthur Keith as Fullerton Professor of the Royal Institution in 1924. He was knighted in 1935. He gave the Croonian Lecture of the Royal Society on foetal respiration (1935) and the Linacre Lecture on respiratory patterns at birth (1941). He was awarded the Copley Medal of the Royal Society in 1943. Shortly before he died, he published his last classical work: *Researches in Prenatal Life*. He described its aim and scope:

> "The aim then of this book is to trace the development of function in the mammalian foetus, never losing sight of the fact that one day the call will come and the foetus will be born. Not only has the foetus to develop a fundamental life which will suffice for intrauterine conditions, but at the same time it has to develop an economy which will understand the shock of birth, and will suffice, nay more than suffice, for its new environment."

This work towards the end of his career was instrumental in establishing the new discipline of perinatal-neonatal Medicine. Joseph Barcroft was a gifted and inspiring teacher, with gentle wit, thoughtful and considerate to his juniors, who regarded him with affection. His distinguished colleague Donald Barron, quoting the American poet, Fitz-Greene Halleck (1790-1867), said of him:

> *"None knew thee but to love thee, nor named thee but to praise."*

Barcroft's involvement with his Quaker heritage was apparent in many of his activities and attitudes, but was perhaps most obvious when between 1902 and 1905 he was a Governor of the Quaker school, Leighton Park in Reading. In 1903 he had married Mary Agnetta Ball daughter of the astronomer, Sir Robert Stawell Ball; they lived in Cambridge. His son Henry Barcroft MD, DSc, FRS, became Professor of Physiology at both Belfast and London; another son Robert, was an army Lt Colonel.

Joseph died of a heart attack on 21 March 1947. His portrait by Walter Benington, is at The National Portrait Gallery (NPG x86261).

Alfred Joseph Clark MD, FRCP, FRS (1885-1941)

Mode of action of drugs on cells; classic textbook

AJ CLARK (Fig. 33) was born on 19 August 1885 in Northover, near Glastonbury, Somerset, the elder son and second of four children of Francis Joseph Clark, (partner in C. and J. Clark Ltd, shoe manufacturers at Street) and his wife, Elizabeth Mary Smithson.[80] As with earlier generations of his Quaker family, his education was

Fig. 33. *AJ Clark.*

at Bootham School, York. He entered King's College, Cambridge, in 1903, and gained first classes in both parts of the natural sciences tripos (1905 and 1907). He then began clinical training and excelled, obtaining the MRCP 1912, MD two years later and the Fellowship (FRCP) in 1921. 'The mode of excretion of haemoglobin and its derivatives' was the title of his M.D. thesis at King's College, Cambridge.

He soon focussed his energies on pharmacology and physiology research. Clark showed that the primary effects of drugs on cells are understandable in terms of the known laws of physical and biological chemistry. This was achieved partly by a classical series of experiments to study the action of the transmitters of nerve impulses (neurotransmitters), acetylcholine and atropine on their targets (receptors). The results were encapsulated in his *The Mode of Action of Drugs on Cells* (1933) an immensely influential monograph. His earlier work on the development of the hypodynamic state in the heart was deemed to be of great importance in connection with recent theories of cardiac function and of nervous influences acting on them. In his papers on the effect of drugs on the heart and other tissues he introduced fresh ideas and techniques into a field of pharmacological research which had long remained sterile. From 1920 to 1926 he held the Chair of pharmacology at University College, London. Then from 1926 until his death he was Professor of Materia Medica at the University of Edinburgh. He was elected FRS in 1931. He was an influential member of the Medical Research Council from 1934.

Clark's textbook *Applied Pharmacology* (1923) was characterized by its physiological and pathophysiological emphasis, by the inclusion of experimental evidence wherever possible, and by its quantitative approach. It achieved no less than eight editions and became required reading for British medical students for over 40 years.

Clark was an austere, shy man of the highest personal standards. Perhaps eschewing his pacifist heritage, he enlisted in the RAMC in World War I where he had 'harrowing experiences' leading to his decoration with the Military Cross. He resigned from the Society of Friends in 1917. Most unusually at the age of 54, he served in World War II, becoming lieutenant colonel. He died suddenly in Edinburgh on 30 July 1941 leaving a wife Beatrice (née Powell) and four children. His portrait in 1931, a bromide print by Walter Stoneman NPG x166556 is in the National Portrait gallery.

CHAPTER 24

Walter Russell Brain DM, FRCP, FRS (1895-1966)

Remote effects of cancer; carpal tunnel syndrome; disorders of language and higher mental functions; classic textbook

RUSSELL BRAIN (Fig. 34) was born at Clovelly, Denmark Road, Reading, on 23 October 1895, the only son of Walter John Brain, solicitor, and his wife, Edith Alice, daughter of Charles Smith, architect. A man of enormous intellect and integrity, he came to the Quaker faith at the age of 36.

Fig. 34. *Walter Russell Brain (Baron Brain of Eynsham).*

At Mill Hill School he studied classics, since he was intended for the law. He however, wanted to learn science, but his parents did not allow this. In 1914 he entered New College, Oxford, as a commoner to read history, which he disliked. Disapproving strongly of war, he joined the Friends' Ambulance Unit in 1915 and was sent to work in York. Moving later to the King George Hospital, London, he became attached to the X-ray department, where he met Stella (b. 1896), daughter of the physician Reginald Langdon Langdon-Down. They married on 8 September 1920. In 1919 he had returned to read Medicine at New College, where he was taught by Julian Huxley and met William Osler. Anxious to qualify and get married, he took a shortened course for the BA (1919) and obtained the Theodore Williams scholarship in physiology (1920). He entered the London Hospital in October 1920, graduated BM BCh (Oxon.) in 1922, proceeded DM in 1925, and was elected FRCP in 1931.

Brain joined the new medical unit at the London Hospital.[81] Through the influence of Henry Head and George Riddoch he took up neurology. He was appointed physician to Maida Vale Hospital in 1925, assistant physician to the London Hospital in 1927, and he was physician to Moorfields Hospital in 1930-37. Brain made many important contributions to neurology.[82] With Dickson Wright and Marcia Wilkinson he showed that the median nerve could be paralysed by compression at the wrist in the carpal tunnel; surgical relief of this would restore function.

With D. W. C. Northfield and Marcia Wilkinson he demonstrated the importance of protrusion of the intervertebral disc in the cervical spine as a cause of paralysis of the legs; this has been recognized as cervical spondylotic myelopathy, a common neurological disturbance.

He described the remote effects (i.e. not caused by secondary deposits) on the brain and peripheral nerves of cancer, particularly cancer of the lung. The British Empire Cancer Campaign therefore, established at the London Hospital a unit for the investigation of carcinomatous neuropathies, which Brain directed until his death. He was an excellent and scholarly physician, more than a laboratory investigator.

Brain had originally considered making a career in psychiatry. He never lost his interest in affairs of the mind, and particularly the problem of perception. *Mind, Perception and Science* (1951), the Riddell lectures on *The Nature of Experience* (1959), and a book, *Speech Disorders* (1961), were the outcome. From the time he was elected to the London Hospital, Brain earned his livelihood as a physician in consulting practice, in which he was very successful. He had a remarkable memory and a flair for lucid yet succinct prose, resulting in a book, *Diseases of the Nervous System*, first published in 1933 and, unusual for a medical textbook, reaching a sixth edition, in 1962. It was almost compulsory reading for post-graduates in Medicine and Neurology.

More discursive books, elegantly written, bearing a subtly reflective quality were to follow: *Some Reflections on Genius, and other Essays* (1960), *Doctors Past and Present* (1964), *Science and Man* (1966), *Tea with Walter de la Mare* (1957), and *Poems and Verses* (1961). He edited the premier neurological journal *Brain* from 1954 till his death.

Lord Brain had a remarkable career culminating in his being elected the President of the British Association for the Advancement of Science, the first practising physician or surgeon to hold that office since Lord Lister. He was an astute clinician and for example, predicted the nature of the inheritance in familial goitre in 1927. It was his clinical case reports, his interests in the brain mind problem in relation to speech and perception which gave rise to his philosophical writings. In the seven years (1950-1957), when President of the Royal College of Physicians, he published 30 papers and two editions of his textbook, and sat on two Royal Commissions. At the same time in 1957, he published *Tea with Walter de la Mare* (cited as a Medical Classic in the September 2008 issue of the BMJ). They were not easy times politically and he was criticized by the BMA. He achieved all this, supported by a time-limited clinical practice, an ease of writing, two secretaries, and importantly the royalties from his successful textbooks. His work was characterised by great industry, the refusal to waste a minute, so that he even dictated and read when travelling in the back of his car.

I remember Lord Brain as a shy, quiet, but kindly man, given to long silences, and at times almost embarrassingly brief but penetrating comments. He once wrote:

'There are two international languages of religion: the Latin of the Roman Catholic Church, and the silence of the Quakers.'

His gracious after dinner speeches, full of wit and learning, often took strangers by surprise.

Russell Brain and Stella Langdon-Down* married after their meeting in the X-ray department. They had two sons and a daughter, to whom they were devoted. They joined the Society of Friends in 1931 and were subsequently regular attenders at the meeting-house on Sundays. He gave the Swarthmore lecture in 1944, '*Man, Society and Religion*', in which he stressed the importance of a social conscience. This conscience of his led him to become chairman of the medical council of the London Hospital during the war, defending the interests of those who were away on active service. He became a member of King Edward's Hospital Fund for London and chairman of its hospital service plan. He attended Churchill as a patient on several occasions.[83] In 1950 he was elected President of the Royal College of Physicians, London, retaining this office until 1957. He was a member of the royal commission on marriage and divorce in 1952, of the royal commission on mental certification and detention in 1954, of the interdepartmental committee on drug addiction in 1958, and became President of the British Association for the Advancement of Science in 1963-4.

He was knighted in 1952, created a baronet in 1954, and made Baron Brain of Eynsham in 1962. He was elected FRS in 1964[84] and an honorary Fellow of New College, Oxford, in 1952. He received honorary degrees from many Universities. and was an honorary member of American, French, German, and Spanish neurological societies, and of the Swiss Academy of Medicine. He gave the Linacre lectures at Cambridge, the Riddell lectures at Durham, the Bryce lecture at Oxford, and the Osler oration in Canada. He was awarded the Osler medal for 1960 at Oxford.

Henry Miller, the erudite witty neurologist, reviewing 'Doctors Past and Present' admirably summarised the man:

"a mind remarkably at home among the literature and philosophy of to-day and yesterday as well as with every aspect of contemporary medicine and science, a mind furthermore in

---

* Granddaughter of Reginald Langdon Langdon-Down, after whom Mongolism or Down's syndrome was named.

which judgments of men and affairs are so balanced, so humane, and so eminently reasonable that one looks in vain and – let us admit it, even with a faint sense of disappointment – for some comforting hint of the kind of prejudice or irrationality which so often colours our own most firmly held opinions."

He died of prostate cancer at his home, Hillmorton, Coombe Hill Road, Kingston, Surrey, on 29 December 1966, working to the end: his last working day was devoted to arranging a new issue of Brain. A meeting in his memory was held at Friends' House, London, on 10 February 1967. He was succeeded to the baronetcy by his elder son, Christopher Langdon (b. 1926). His younger son, Michael, who attended Leighton Park School, became Professor of Medicine at McMaster University, Ontario.

CHAPTER 25

Alan Lloyd Hodgkin PhD, DSc., FRS (1914-1998)

Transmission of the nerve impulse: the ionic mechanisms involved in excitation and inhibition of the nerve cell membrane

CONTRIBUTIONS TO the diagnosis and treatment of illness are not confined to those privileged clinicians who have day to day care of the sick. Those physiologists, pathologists and others who labour in laboratories of various kinds, make discoveries about the mechanisms of diseases and the agents employed in their treatment, which confer practical benefits in the management of illness. We

Fig. 35. *Sir Alan Lloyd Hodgkin.*

have already referred to several such researchers; none was more important in his discoveries than Alan Hodgkin (Fig. 35).

Born at Banbury near Oxford, into a long heritage of Quakers, Hodgkin attended The Down's school, then Gresham's school in Holt. His grandfather, Thomas Hodgkin, and uncle, Robin Hodgkin, were historians and Alan at first equivocated between history and science. His great-great uncle was Thomas Hodgkin MD,FRS and his great-great grandfather was Luke Howard FRS. (vide supra) Dorothy Hodgkin OM, FRS was the wife of his cousin, Thomas Lionel Hodgkin. With such a family history, one might wonder about the roles of heredity and environment in the genesis of achievement. Alan studied biology and chemistry, and graduated from Trinity College, Cambridge and became a Fellow in 1936. He was fortunate, for at that time the high table of Trinity included an astonishing array of scientific talent, which included J. J. Thomson, Rutherford, Aston, Eddington, Hopkins, G. H. Hardy and Adrian. In the Physiological Laboratory he learnt about cable-theory from Rushton and about amplifiers from Matthews, Grey Walter and Rawdon-Smith.

A. V. Hill sponsored him and arranged work with the internationally renowned Gasser at the Rockefeller Institute, New York in 1937-8. There he worked with K. S. Cole at Woods Hole and learnt how to dissect squid axons. He returned to Cambridge in 1938 and in the following year started a collaboration with A. F. Huxley, whom he had the good fortune to teach. Huxley recorded:

> "Hodgkin went to Plymouth and invited me to join him and between us we managed to get fibres set up so we could get an electrode down inside them; [this] enabled us to record the impulse from the inside of the squid fibre without distortion".

This was interrupted by World War II when he worked on radar for the Air Ministry. He resumed his work with Huxley after the end of the war and his discoveries led to the FRS in 1948. Most of the experiments on giant nerve fibres were done at the Laboratory of the Marine Biological Association, Plymouth, where he usually spent two or three months each year.

In 1951, with Andrew Huxley and Bernard Katz, he worked out the sodium theory to explain the difference in action and resting potentials in nerve fibres. Using the single nerve fibre (giant axon) of a squid, they were able to demonstrate that there is an exchange of sodium and potassium ions between the cell and its surroundings during a nervous impulse, which enables the nerve fibre to carry a further impulse. The result is known as The *Hodgkin-Huxley model* that describes how nerve impulses, known as action potentials in neurons are initiated and propagated. Hodgkin also showed that the nerve fibre's potential for electrical conduction was greater during the actual passage of an impulse than when the fibre was resting. For their "discoveries concerning the ionic mechanisms involved in excitation and inhibition in the peripheral and central portions of the nerve cell membrane", Hodgkin, Huxley, and John Eccles shared the Nobel Prize for Physiology or Medicine in 1963.[85] The main findings, Hodgkin published in *Conduction of the Nervous Impulse* (1964). The work led the to the hypothesis of *ion channels*, which was confirmed by Neher and Sakmann's studies, recognised by a Nobel prize in 1991.

At the physiological laboratory at Cambridge, Hodgkin served as Foulerton Research Professor from 1952 to 1969, and as Professor of Biophysics from 1970 until 1981. Between 1978 and 1984, he was master of Trinity College, Cambridge. In 1992, he published his autobiography *Chance and Design: Reminiscences of Science in Peace and War* (Cambridge University Press, Cambridge, 1992). He was knighted in 1972, and awarded the much prized Order of Merit in 1973. From 1970 to 1975, he was President of the Royal Society.

How much did his long Quaker heritage affect him? In the elegantly penned *Chance and Design,* Hodgkin speaks of a colleague's "considerable influence on my life by softening the strongly puritanical streak I had acquired from my Quaker upbringing" (p.70). Although when at Cambridge he distributed pacifist leaflets of which he approved, he tells how his Communist friends set about trying to remove his religious beliefs, and says: "This was not very difficult because I had begun to have serious doubts about most of the central aspects of the religion which I found incompatible with my scientific knowledge." He likewise rejected Marxism (p.83). With irony, he remarks: "the serious minded ways in which I passed my free time was about all that was left of my Quaker heritage" (p.93). He also relinquished notions of pacifism when he joined the RAF. We can conclude that he was always aware of this component of his background, but he avoided formal religious commitments, which he failed to accommodate with his scientific knowledge of the world.

While at the Rockefeller Institute in 1938 he met Peyton Rous, the Nobel Prize winning pathologist. He married his daughter, Marion Rous in 1944, and they settled in Cambridge. They had three daughters. The eldest, Sarah Hayes is a writer and illustrator. The second, Deborah worked in psychology and neurobiology, and the third, Rachel Hodgkin, works in children's law.* Their son, Jonathan is Professor of Genetics in the department of Biochemistry, Oxford, and yet another Hodgkin who is a FRS!

CHAPTER 26

Lionel Sharples Penrose MD, FRCP, FRS (1898-1972)

Genetics of mental deficiency; anti war campaigner

LIONEL PENROSE (Fig. 36) was born at 44 Finchley Road, London, on 11 June 1898 of Quaker stock, the second of the four sons of James Doyle Penrose an artist and his wife, Elizabeth Josephine. Sir Roland Algernon Penrose (1900-1984), a famous surrealist artist, was his brother. Lionel attended the Downs School, and the Quaker, Leighton Park School, whence he joined the

Fig. 36. *Lionel Sharples Penrose.*

Friends' ambulance service, serving in France from 1916 till the end of the First World War. He gained a place to read the moral sciences at St John's College, Cambridge and gained a first in part two of the tripos in 1921 and was awarded the Newcombe prize. After a year's postgraduate work in psychology at Cambridge he travelled to Vienna, stayed for two years, pondering the problems of mental illness. But lack of medical training was a serious handicap and so he managed to get a place for clinical studies at St Thomas's Hospital, where he qualified MRCS, LRCP in 1928 and gained the Bristowe medal (1929). He then carried out work on schizophrenia, which yielded an MD thesis in 1930.

The Royal Eastern Counties Institution at Colchester, was an asylum for mentally defective* patients. Penrose decided in 1931 to investigate the diverse problems they posed for humanitarian reasons of a very common and neglected problem. He used his own nonverbal "pattern perception" test to discriminate between mentally ill and otherwise unaffected individuals and to compare parental and offspring IQs. Over seven years he made a detailed study of 1280 mentally defective patients and their 6629 siblings, parents and families that formed the basis of his work. It was published in a Medical Research Council Special Report, and later in two books, *Mental Defect* (1933) and three editions later *The Biology of Mental Defect* (1949),[86] the last in 1972. They were unsurpassed in their time for the wealth of original scientific, biological, and genetic information that they contained. This work shaped Penrose's own research career and created a lasting legacy on these subjects.

During World War II Penrose was director of psychiatric research in Ontario, Canada. He returned home to be appointed Galton Professor of Eugenics at University College, London. He said it was "irksome" to be the head of a department of Eugenics and to edit a journal with Eugenics in its title without ever studying or writing a word about eugenics! But it was not until 1954 that he managed to change the title of the journal from Annals of Eugenics to Annals of Human Genetics, and not until 1963 did his Chair became the Galton Professorship of Human Genetics. He

---

* The terms: Mental defect or mental deficiency are sometimes now deemed politically incorrect. Alternative terms used are mental retardation, mental subnormality, and developmental delay.

clarified the genetics and inheritance of mental defect, particularly Mongolism (for which he favoured the now popular term Down's syndrome or anomaly). His monograph in 1966 coincided with the centenary of John Langdon Haydon Langdon-Down's (1828-1896) first description of the condition.[87]

A versatile researcher, Penrose used the new techniques of chromosome counting and analysis which he related to a variety of genetic illnesses during the 1950s and '60s. His methods permitted striking advances in human genetics. The distillate of his work, *Outline of Human Genetics* (1960) ran to three editions in 13 years. He became an expert in examining finger and palm prints, or dermatoglyphs – of diagnostic value in some mental illnesses. The diagnosis and treatment of inherited phenylketonuria, a cause of mental subnormality, was also fertile ground in which he made valuable contributions.

He retired in 1965 but continued to work at the Kennedy-Galton Centre at Harperbury Hospital. He expanded current statistical methods, estimated the mutation rate of a human gene, obtained evidence for several linkages for maternal inheritance, and noted effects of maternal age. From his research department emerged no less than 108 published papers and books by the time he was elected FRS on 19 March, 1953. His reputation may be inferred from his illustrious proposers for the FRS 'From personal know-ledge': J. B. S. Haldane; Lancelot Hogben; Julian S. Huxley; P. B. Medawar; S. C. Harland; R. A. Fisher.

Penrose's work gained international recognition.[88] He was awarded many honorary degrees, the international award of the Joseph P. Kennedy Foundation (1964), and the James Calvert Spence medal in paediatrics (1964). He was President of the Genetical Society of Great Britain (1955-8). He was elected Fellow of the Royal College of Physicians, London in 1962, and of the Royal College of Psychiatrists in 1971.

Apart from Penrose's genetics work, an enduring interest was his opposition to war, both on moral and practical grounds. He believed war was analogous to disease and could be dealt with scientifically, though he later had to qualify this view.[88] When the Korean war threatened a worldwide conflict he set out to found, and for ten years was President of, the Medical Association for the Prevention of War. A touching personal account was written by

Renata Laxova.[90] It was said of him that the combination of high intelligence, modesty, and a sense of humour made him an agreeable companion.

He had a lasting interest in mathematical puzzles. With his son Roger, he constructed "a self reproducible machine", published in Nature, 1957. He created multiple wooden and other puzzles, among them Puzzles for Christmas, published together with Roger (in the New Scientist 1958) "to provide mental stimulation during the academic vacation". The publication included the "impossible staircase" (a famous theme in the work of Dutch artist Max Escher) originated by the Penroses.

He married Margaret, daughter of Prof J. B. Leathes, FRS. They had four children: Sir Roger Penrose FRS, one of two mathematics Professors, a chess master, and a paediatrician. He died at the General Hospital, Harlesdon Road, Willesden, London, on 12 May 1972.

CHAPTER 27

Conclusion

THIS HIGHLY selective exploration of the lives and achievements of some celebrated Quakers of Britain is at best a superficial sampling. Although criteria for election may have been slightly less stringent in the 18th and 19th centuries, it is notable how many were elected as Fellows of the Royal Society, how many were considerable experts in natural history and established collections of ancient remnants, and how many showed unusual generosity in their acts of philanthropy. There are many other Quaker scientists and doctors with similar achievements, who are well documented in other books and literary documents. If those considered here have a common thread, it may be that they share the understated, practical philosophy of their faith, well described in the statement that *"Quakers share a way of life rather than a set of beliefs"*. Nuland's unstinting encomium about Joseph Lister clearly highlights this view, and paints a picture, which could be extended to many of the other doctors and scientists mentioned here:

> There seems to have been a quality about him that was so warmly, serenely, gently strong that words like "dignity," "forbearance... integrity... sweetness," and "honor" only leave his biographers as beggared for description as they did his contemporaries. His opponents admired him, and even his most relentless antagonists, fulminate against his theories though they might, spoke not a harsh word about the man himself. There was a flavor of simple goodness in his life, flowing evenly from the philosophical spring of a distinctive faith that has nourished the spirit of more than a few of the moral leaders of the past three hundred years. The source of that spring is to be

found in the ethical principles of the Religious Society of Friends.

Though their religious creeds undoubtedly influenced their attitudes to patients, illness, and the fate of the underprivileged, it would be naïve to claim that their faith and beliefs were directly responsible for their medical and scientific attainments. But a heritage of prohibition from formal academic centres was probably an important spur to their quest for knowledge – despite these formidable issues. Indeed, many managed eventually to secure their education, but often only by enduring irrational restrictions and by surmounting seemingly impossible obstacles.

The much argued and fascinating general arguments and discussions relating science to religion are unresolved. In essence, some assert that the religious spirit or inner light is conducive to the search for scientific truths; whilst others insist that religion, a matter of objectively untestable personal belief, is quite distinct from the observation and the logical deductive processes that define science. These polemics can be posed to Quakerism and science, but their resolution is beyond the scope of this essay.

The physicians and scientists portrayed here have in large measure shown considerable native gifts and often inherited talents, but their lives and work also show as recurring themes, a deeply rooted imaginative search for scientific truths, unrelenting industry, modesty, and amazing acts of philanthropy. Even if one was to foolishly discount their religious beliefs and adherence, they are in any view, exemplary lives that pose a perpetual challenge to those who would follow. John Fothergill, in a letter to Dr William Cuming, Dec 8, 1769, expressed these sentiments far more eloquently:

Let us preserve the memory of the deserving: perhaps it may prompt others likewise to deserve.

The contributions of these men and women to the essential humanity, art, and science of Medicine are their lasting testimony.

Appendix 1

FOR FURTHER reference, the archives of the Religious Society Of Friends in London contains collections of autograph letters containing by members of the medical profession, which include William Allen (1770-1843); Martin Barry (1802-55); Joseph Gurney Bevan (1753-1814), druggist; Peter Collinson (1694-1768); John Dalton (1766-1844); Thomas Dimsdale (1712-1800); John Fothergill (1712-80); Thomas Hancock (1783-1849); Charles Marshall (1637-98), medical practitioner; Thomas Pole (1753-1829); and many others.

Appendix 2

Selection of entries in the Dictionary of National Biography whose practice is Medicine and religious affiliation: Quaker*

Ashby, Henry (1846-1908), paediatrician.

Barcroft, Sir Joseph (1872-1947), physiologist.

Barry, Martin (1802-1855), microscopist and embryologist.

Bentham, Ethel (1861-1931), physician and politician.

Bevan, Silvanus (1691-1765), apothecary.

Birkbeck, George (1776-1841), physician and educationist.

Blaschko, Hugh [formerly Karl Felix Hermann] (1900-1993), biochemist and pharmacologist.

Bradley, Thomas (c. 1751-1813), physician.

Brain, Walter Russell, first Baron Brain (1895-1966), physician and medical administrator.

Brocklesby, Richard (1722-1797), physician.

Brown, Joseph (1784-1868), physician.

Clark, Alfred Joseph (1885-1941), pharmacologist.

Clark, Hilda (1881-1955), physician and humanitarian aid worker.

Creak, (Eleanor) Mildred (1898-1993), child psychiatrist.

Dimsdale, Thomas (1712-1800), physician.

Faber, Albert Otto (1612-1684), chemical physician.

Fothergill, John (1712-1780), physician and naturalist.

Fox, Wilson (1831-1887), physician.

Godlee, Sir Rickman John, baronet (1849-1925), surgeon.

Hancock, Thomas (1783-1849), physician.

Head, Sir Henry (1861-1940), neurologist.

Heaf, Frederick Rowland George [formerly Fritz Rudolf Georg Hief] (1894-1973), physician.

Helmont, Franciscus Mercurius van, baron of Helmont and Merode in the nobility of the Holy Roman empire (1614-1698), physician and cabbalist.

Hillary, William (1697-1763), physician.

Hodgkin, Sir Alan Lloyd (1914-1998), physiologist.

Hodgkin, Thomas (1798-1866), physician and social reformer.

Hutchinson, Sir Jonathan (1828-1913), surgeon.

Knight, Elizabeth (1869-1933), doctor and campaigner for women's suffrage.

Lettsom, John Coakley (1744-1815), physician and philanthropist.

Lister, Joseph, Baron Lister (1827-1912), surgeon and founder of a system of antiseptic surgery.

Lower, Thomas (bap. 1633, d. 1720), Quaker activist and physician.

Moore, Sir Norman, first baronet (1847-1922), physician and Irish scholar.

Morland, Egbert Coleby (1874-1955), physician and writer on medicine.

Mottram, Vernon Henry (1882-1976), physiologist and nutritionist.

Newman, Sir George (1870-1948), medical officer of health.

Overend, Hall (1772-1831), surgeon apothecary and teacher of medicine.

Peacock, Thomas Bevill (1812-1882), physician.

Penrose, Lionel Sharples (1898-1972), physician.

Pole, Thomas (1753-1829), physician and Quaker minister.

Power, Sir D'Arcy (1855-1941), surgeon and historian.

Prichard, James Cowles (1786-1848), physician and ethnologist.

Rutty, John (1698-1775), physician.

Salter, Alfred (1873-1945), medical practitioner and politician.

Sims, John (1749-1831), physician and botanist.

Sinton, John Alexander (1884-1956), soldier and malariologist.

Thompson, Gilbert (1728-1803), physician.

Thurnam, John (1810-1873), psychiatrist and ethnologist.

Tuke, Samuel (1784-1857), asylum reformer and philanthropist.

Walker, George Alfred (1807-1884), physician, sanitary reformer.

Walker, John (1759-1830), vaccinator and writer.

Walton, Arthur (1897-1959), physiologist.

Whitehead, John (1739/40-1804), physician and biographer.

Willan, Robert (1757-1812), physician and dermatologist.

Woodhead, Sir German Sims (1855-1921), pathologist and health campaigner.

Woodville, William (1752-1805), physician and botanist.

Young, Thomas (1773-1829), physician and natural philosopher.

* I am indebted to Jennifer Milligan, Library of the Religious Society of Friends for this information.

References

1. Cantor GN. Quakers, Jews, and Science: Religious Responses to Modernity and the Sciences in Britain, 1650-1900. Oxford University Press, 2005.
2. Thompson, Silvanus Phillips. The Quest for Truth. Swarthmore Lecture 1915. Nature, 1917; 100 (2509): 243.
3. Sharpless K. Barry. Searching For New Reactivity. Nobel Lecture, December 8, 2001 Nobel Lectures, Chemistry 1963-1970, Elsevier Publishing Company, Amsterdam, 1972.
4. Elmer P. Medicine, Science and the Quakers: the 'Puritanism-science' debate reconsidered. J Friends Hist Soc. 1981; 54: 273-80.
5. Raistrick, A. Quakers in science and industry : being an account of the Quaker contributions to science and industry during the 17th and 18th centuries / 1896-1991. – 1993. Newton Abbott. David & Charles, 1968.
6. Cantor G. Quakers in The Royal Society, 1660-1750. Notes and Records of the Royal Society, 1997; 51: 175-93. See also Ref 1. Pp. 2-8.
7. Roscoe H.E., John Dalton and the Rise of Modern Chemistry. New York and London, Macmillan and Co., 1895.
8. Robinson, Andrew. The Last Man Who Knew Everything: Thomas Young, the Anonymous Polymath Who Proved Newton Wrong, Explained How We See, Cured the Sick and Deciphered the Rosetta Stone Among Other Feats of Genius. New York: Pi Press 2006.
9. Crichton Browne J. Thomas Young. In: Stray leaves from a physician's portfolio. No Date. Hodder & Stoughton. First edn [probably written circa 1927] pp.298-328.
10. Nicolle, Margaret. William Allen: Quaker Friend of Lindfield (1770-1843).
11. Childs PE. The life and work of Dame Kathleen Lonsdale (1903-1971). A Lecture to mark the official opening of the Kathleen Lonsdale Building, University of Limerick 20th. April 1998. http://www.ul.ie/~childsp/Elements/Issue4/childs.htm
12. Reville W. Kathleen Lonsdale – Famous Irish Scientist. The Irish Times, December 13, 2001.

13. Hodgkin D. Kathleen Lonsdale: A Biographical Memoir. Published by the Royal Society, 1976.
14. Lonsdale Kathleen. Crystals and X-rays. G. Bell, 1948.
15. Ferry, G. Dorothy Hodgkin. A life. London 1998.
16. The Nobel Prize in Chemistry 1964, Perspectives From Nobel Lectures, Chemistry 1963-1970, Elsevier Publishing Company, Amsterdam, 1972.
17. Hodgkin, Dorothy Crowfoot: The X-ray analysis of complicated molecules. Nobel Lecture, December 11, 1964.
18. Howard J A K. Nature Reviews. Molecular Cell Biology. London: Nov 2003. Vol. 4, Iss. 11; p. 891-6.
19. Lewy FH. The first authentic case of major trigeminal neuralgia and some comments on the history of this disease. Ann Med Hist 1938; 10 : 247-50.
20. Pearce JMS. Trigeminal neuralgia (Fothergill's disease) in the 17th and 18th centuries. J. Neurol. Neurosurg. Psychiatry 2003 74(12): p. 1688
21. Fothergill J. Remarks on that complaint commonly known under the name of sick headach, in : Medical observations and inquiries by A Society of Physicians in London, 1784; 6: 103-137.
22. DeLacy M. Fothergill, John (1712-1780), physician and naturalist DNB. Oxford, OUP 2004 (Sept).
23. Elkinton JR. Betty Fothergill and her "Uncle Doctor". An intimate glimpse of Dr. John Fothergill. Ann Intern Med. 1976; 85: 637-40.
24. Fox RH. Dr John Fothergill and his friends. 1919. Pp.265
25. Booth CC. John Haygarth, FRS (1740-1827): A Physician of the Enlightenment. American Philosophical Society, 2005
26. Hunting P. The Medical Society of London. Postgraduate Medical Journal 2004; 80: 350-354.
27. McConaghy M. D., Silberman M, Kalashnikova I. Penn in the 18th Century. An exhibit first appeared on the Web in 2004. http://www.archives.upenn.edu/histy/features/1700s/med_fac.html
28. Pinel P. Treatise on Insanity. 1801. Translation by Davis DD. reprinted : New York: Hafner Publishing; 1962.
29. Pearce JMS. The West Riding Lunatic Asylum. J Neurol Neurosurg Psychiatry 2003; 74 1141
30. Sessions Willam K, Sessions E. Margaret. The Tukes of York in the Seventeenth, Eighteenth and Nineteenth Centuries Ebor Press, York. 1971.
31. Pearce J M S The West Riding Lunatic Asylum. J Neurol Neurosurg Psychiatry 2003; 74 1141
32. Daniel Hack Tuke, obituary, Br Med J. 1895; March 9; 1 (1784): 565-566.
33. Clarke J. F. Autobiographical Recollections of the Medical Profession, London, 1874, 331.

34. Hodgkin T. On some morbid appearances of the absorbent glands and spleen. Medico-Chirurgical Transactions, London, 1832; 17: 68-114. Hodgkin's disease. Reproduced in Medical Classics, 1937, 1: 741-740.

35. Wilks S. Case of a peculiar enlargement of the lymphatic glands frequently associated with disease of the spleen. Guy's Hosp Reports 1856 3 ser, 2: 114-32 and 1865. 11: 56-67.

36. Hardwick C. Thomas Hodgkin 1798-1866. Guys Hosp Rep. 1966; 115: 255-61.

37. Houston JC, Knox R. Guy's Hospital reports: special number dedicated to Thomas Hodgkin (1798-1866). 1966.

38. Pearce JMS. Historical note. Richard Bright & his neurological studies. Eur Neurology 2008; in the press.

39. Pearce JMS. Thomas Addison (1793-1860). J Royal Soc Med. 2004; 97(6): 297-300.

40. Rosenfeld LR. Thomas Hodgkin, Morbid anatomist and social activist. New York, London, Madison books. 1993.

41. Creighton Louise. Life and letters of Thomas Hodgkin. / Hodgkin, Thomas, 1831-1913; & 1850-1936. – 1918

42. King R. Obituary of Thomas Hodgkin, M.D., 1867 Royal Anthropological Institute of Great Britain and Ireland 1867; 341-3.

43. Kass AM, and Kass EM. Perfecting the world: the life and times of Dr. Thomas Hodgkin 1798-1866. Boston: Harcourt Brace Jovanovich, 1988.

44. Stone MJ. Thomas Hodgkin: medical immortal and uncompromising idealist. Proc (Baylor Univ Med Cent). 2005; 18(4): 368-375.

45. Wilson, Dorothy Clarke. Lone woman: the story of Elizabeth Blackwell, the first woman doctor. Boston, Little Brown. 1970.

46. Roth N. The personalities of two pioneer medical women: Elizabeth Blackwell and Elizabeth Garrett Anderson. Bull N Y Acad Med. 1971; 47(1): 67-79.

47. Boyd Julia. The Excellent Doctor Blackwell: The Life of the First Female Physician. Stroud, Gloucestershire, Sutton Pub., 2005.

48. Godlee Sir Rickman John. Lord Lister. London. Macmillan 1917.

49. Nuland Sherwin B. Doctors: The Biography of Medicine. 2nd edn New York. Second Vintage Books. 1995. Pp.343-386.

50. Pasteur L. Mémoire sur la fermentation appelée lactique. Compte Rendu. Acad Sci, Paris 1857; 45: 913-6. [this classic was expanded in several subsequent papers]

51. Lister J. On the lactic fermentation and its bearing on pathology. Trans path Soc London 1877-78; 29: 425-67.

52. Lister Joseph (1827-1912): Antiseptic Principle Of The Practice Of Surgery, 1867.

53. Lister J. On a New Method of Treating Compound Fracture, Abscess, Etc. The Lancet 1867; i: 326, 357, 387, 507. And, Illustrations of the Antiseptic System of Treatment in Surgery. *ibid* 1867; 2: 668.

54. Lister J. Effects of the antiseptic system of treatment upon the salubrity of a surgical hospital. Lancet 1870; 1: 40-42. See also Lister Joseph, 1st Baron Lister. Collected papers. 2 vols. Oxford, Clarendon press, 1909.

55. Treves GF. Cited by Sherwin B Nuland ref: 49.

56. Lister, Joseph. In: Plarr's Lives of the Fellows Online. http://livesonline.rcseng.ac.uk/biogs/E000500b.htm

57. Pearce JMS. Sir Jonathan Hutchinson (1828-1913) An early description of temporal arteritis. J Neurology Neurosurgery Psychiatry 1994; 57: 216.

58. James DG. Centenary commemoration of sarcoidosis and of Jonathan Hutchinson. Br Med J. 1969; 2: 109-110.

59. Faces behind ophthalmic eponyms. [Jonathan Hutchinson] http://www.mrcophth.com/ophthalmologyhalloffame/hutchinson.html

60. Pearce JMS. The First Attempts at Removal of Brain Tumours. In: Historical Aspects of the Neuroscience, a Festschrift for Macdonald Critchley. eds F Clifford Rose and WF Bynum. p 239-43. New York, Raven Press 1981.

61. Godlee R. British Masters Of Ophthalmology Series: No. 15. – Sir Jonathan Hutchinson, F.R.S., 1828-1913. Br. J. Ophthalmology 1925; 9: 257-81.

62. Pearce JMS. Sir Jonathan Hutchinson (1828-1913) An early description of temporal arteritis. J Neurology Neurosurgery Psychiatry 1994; 57: 216.

63. Hutchinson J. Clinical lecture on heredito-syphilitic struma: and on the teeth as a means of diagnosis. Brit Med J 1861; 1: 515-17.

64. Pearce JMS. The First Attempts At Removal Of Brain Tumours. In: Historical Aspects of the Neuroscience, a Festschrift for Macdonald Critchley. eds F Clifford Rose and WF Bynum. p 239-43. New York, Raven Press 1981.

65. Pearce JMS. Sturge-Weber syndrome (encephalotrigeminal or leptomeningeal angiomatosis). J Neurol Neurosurg Psychiatry. 2006; 77: 1291-2.

66. Sturge W. A. A case of partial epilepsy, apparently due to a lesion of one of the vasomotor centres of the brain. Transactions of the Clinical Society of London, 1879; 12: 162-7.

67. Barlow T. William Allen Sturge. Brit Med J 1919; 1: (April 12): 468-9.

68. Pearce JMS. Henry Head. Journal of Neurology Neurosurgery & Psychiatry 2000; 69: 578

69. Critchley M. The Black Hole and other Essays. London, Pitman 1964. pp.98-107.

70. Head H, Campbell AW. The pathology of herpes zoster and its bearing on sensory localization. Brain. 1900; 23: 353-529.

71. Holmes GM. Obituary, Sir Henry Head. British Medical Journal 1940; 2: 539-41.
72. Obituary. George Newman. Lancet, 5 June 1948: 888.
73. Storey GO, Smith H. Sir George Newman (1870-1948). Journal of Medical Biography 2005, 13: 31-8.
74. Sir Joseph Barcroft: The 20th Century's Renaissance Perinatal Physiologist Neonatal Reviews 2007; 8 No. 8 e311.
75. Dunn PM. Sir Joseph Barcroft of Cambridge (1872-1947) and prenatal research. Arch Dis Child Fetal Neonatal Ed 2000; 82: F75-F76.
76. Roughton FJW. Joseph Barcroft 1872-1947. Royal Society of Obstetrics Notices 1948; 6: 315-45.
77. Barcroft J. Features in the Architecture of Physiological Function Cambridge at the University Press. 1934.
78. Barcroft J. Respiratory Function of the Blood: Part I & II Haemoglobin: Lessons From High Altitudes. Cambridge at the University Press. 1925.
79. Barcroft J. Research on prenatal life. Part I. Oxford: Blackwell Scientific Publications, 1947.
80. Clark, DH. Alfred Joseph Clark 1885-1941: a memoir. [Street, Somerset], C. & J. Clark Ltd Archives, for British Pharmacological Society, 1985.
81. Howie J. Portraits from Memory 17. – Sir Walter Russell Brain, FRS, PRCP (later Lord Brain) British Medical Journal 1987; 295: 108-9.
82. Royal College of Physicians Archives: Walter Russell Brain (1895-1966), 1st Baron Brain of Eynsham: personal and professional papers 1907-66 MSS 3133-3296.
83. Brain, MC. W. Russell Brain, "Encounters with Winston Churchill", Medical History, vol. 44, 2000, 3-20.
84. Pickering, G. W. Biography; Brain, W. Russell, 1895-1966. In: Biographical memoirs of Fellows of the Royal Society, vol. 14, November 1968.
85. Nobel Lectures, Physiology or Medicine 1963-1970, Elsevier Publishing Company, Amsterdam, 1972.
86. Penrose, L. S. The Biology of Mental Defect. With a Pref. By J.B.S. Haldane. Sidgwick & Jackson. London 1949. 4th edn. 1949.
87. Cooke AM. Penrose, Lionel Sharples (1898-1972), rev., Oxford Dictionary of National Biography, Oxford University Press, 2004 [http://www.oxforddnb.com/view/article/31537].
88. Munk's roll. of the Royal College of Physicians of London, Ed. Gordon Wolstenholme. Oxford, IRL Press. 1982; Vol 6. Pp375-7.
89. Harris H. Lionel Sharples Penrose, 1898-1972. Biographical Memoirs of Fellows of the Royal Society, 1973, 19: 521-261. [contains complete bibliography]
90. Laxova R. Lionel Sharples Penrose, 1898-1972: A Personal Memoir in Celebration of the Centenary of His Birth. Genetics 1998; 150: 1333-1340.